经典的回声·ECHO OF CLASSICS

中国古代短篇小说选
STORIES OF OLD CHINA

（唐）蒋　防　　等著

颜惠庆　　译

Written by Jiang Fang and others
Translated by W. W. Yen, Litt. D.

外文出版社
FOREIGN LANGUAGES PRESS

图书在版编目（CIP）数据

中国古代短篇小说选 / 颜惠庆译.
—北京：外文出版社，2003．7
ISBN 7-119-02895-2

I. 中… II. 颜… III. 英语—对照读物，小说
—汉、英

IV. H319.4:I

中国版本图书馆 CIP 数据核字（2001）第 042704 号

外文出版社网址：
 http://www.flp.com.cn
外文出版社电子信箱：
 info@flp.com.cn
 sales@flp.com.cn

中国古代短篇小说选

作　　者　（唐）蒋　防　等
译　　者　颜惠庆
责任编辑　杨春燕
封面设计　席恒青
印刷监制　张国祥
出版发行　外文出版社
社　　址　北京市百万庄大街 24 号　　　邮政编码　100037
电　　话　（010）68320579（总编室）
　　　　　（010）68329514 / 68327211（推广发行部）
印　　刷　三河市汇鑫印务有限公司
经　　销　新华书店 / 外文书店
开　　本　大 32 开
字　　数　160 千字
印　　张　7.75
版　　次　2003 年 8 月第 1 版第 1 次印刷
装　　别　平装
书　　号　ISBN 7-119-02895-2 / I·701（外）
定　　价　13.60 元

出 版 前 言

　　本社专事外文图书的编辑出版,几十年来用英文翻译出版了大量的中国文学作品和文化典籍,上自先秦,下迄现当代,力求全面而准确地反映中国文学及中国文化的基本面貌和灿烂成就。这些英译图书均取自相关领域著名的、权威的作品,英译则出自国内外译界名家。每本图书的编选、翻译过程均极其审慎严肃,精雕细琢,中文作品及相应的英译版本均堪称经典。

　　我们意识到,这些英译精品,不单有对外译介的意义,而且对国内英文学习者、爱好者及英译工作者,也是极有价值的读本。为此,我们对这些英译精品做了认真的遴选,编排成汉英对照的形式,陆续推出,以飨读者。

外文出版社

Publisher's Note

Foreign Languages Press is dedicated to the editing, translating and publishing of books in foreign languages. Over the past several decades it has published, in English, a great number of China's classics and records as well as literary works from the Qin down to modern times, in the aim to fully display the best part of the Chinese culture and its achievements. These books in the original are famous and authoritative in their respective fields, and their English translations are masterworks produced by notable translators both at home and abroad. Each book is carefully compiled and translated with minute precision. Consequently, the English versions as well as their Chinese originals may both be rated as classics.

It is generally considered that these English translations are not only significant for introducing China to the outside world but also useful reading materials for domestic English learners and translators. For this reason, we have carefully selected some of these books, and will publish them successively in Chinese-English bilingual form.

Foreign Languages Press

目　录
CONTENTS

中国古代短篇小说选

STORIES OF OLD CHINA

霍小玉传

大历中,陇西李生名益,年二十,以进土擢第。其明年,拔萃,俟试于天官。夏六月,至长安,舍于新昌里。生门族清华,少有才思,丽词嘉句,时谓无双;先达丈人,翕然推伏。每自矜风调,思得佳偶,博求名妓,久而未谐。

长安有媒鲍十一娘者,故薛驸马家青衣也;折券从良,十余年矣。性便辟,巧言语,豪家戚里,无不经过,追风挟策,推为渠帅。当受

THE HEARTLESS LOVER
Jiang Fang

During that period of the Tang Dynasty known as Da Li there lived in Gansu a young scholar by the name of Li Yi. He had barely reached twenty years of age when he obtained the much coveted doctorate in the imperial examinations, and the following summer in the sixth moon he arrived at Changan, the capital of the empire, for the civil service examination, taking lodgings in the Street of New Prosperity. Li Yi came from a renowned literary family. He was possessed of a brilliant intellect, and was particularly accomplished as a poet and essayist, unequalled in reputation by any other scholar of his time.

Highly pleased with himself and his literary attainments, he had only one regret, and that was his inability to find a congenial and accomplished girl after his own heart. He roved a great deal among the famous courtesans of the city, hoping to meet a sweetheart acceptable to his taste and worthy of his love, but a prolonged hunt resulted in nothing.

At this stage, there lived in Changan a well-known mistress of courtesans and matchmaker, Mrs. Bao, a former bondmaid in the house of one of the emperor's sons-in-law, who had bought her freedom and had been married for a dozen years or so. She was a crafty woman, clever of speech and acquainted with all the distinguished families of the city

生诚托厚赂,意颇德之。经数月,李方闲居舍
之南亭。申未间,忽闻扣门甚急,云是鲍十一
娘至。摄衣从之,迎问曰:"鲍卿今日何故忽然
而来?"鲍笑曰:"苏姑子作好梦也未? 有一仙
人,谪在下界,不邀财货,但慕风流。如此色
目。共十郎相当矣。"生闻之惊跃,神飞体轻,
引鲍手且拜且谢曰:"一生作奴,死亦不惮。"因
问其名居。鲍具说曰:"故霍王小女,字小玉,
王甚爱之。母曰净持。净持,即王之宠婢也。
王之初薨,诸弟兄以其出自贱庶,不甚收录。
因分与资财,遣居于外,易姓为郑氏,人亦不知
其王女。姿质秾艳,一生未见,高情逸态,事事

— in fact, the queen of her profession. Entrusted by Mr. Li with the task of finding for him a lady friend and loaded with valuable presents from him, she tried her best to fulfil his yearning.

One late afternoon as the young scholar was whiling away his time in an arbour of the garden of his house, someone knocked impatiently at the gate. The janitor opened it and reported to him that the caller was Mrs. Bao. Li hurriedly went forward and received her.

"How is it, Madame, that you are here?" he asked.

"Your fondest dream has come true," she said. "A goddess has been banished to this sorry earth: she seeks no wealth but only love and romance. Such beauty and sentiment fulfil all your requirements."

"I am willing to be her slave all my life," cried the young scholar, dancing with delight and seizing Mrs. Bao's hands to show his gratefulness. He asked for her name and address.

"She is Miss Jade, the youngest daughter of the late Prince Huo," she explained. "Her mother, by the name of Purity, was a favourite bondmaid and, later, concubine of His Highness, and when he died, his legitimate heirs considered the girl as born of a woman of humble status and refused to recognize her. The mother was given some money and sent away. She changed her name to Zheng, thus concealing her and the girl's antecedents. She is the most beautiful young woman I have ever laid my eyes on, noble in her sentiments and artistic in her temperament — in short, superior in every way. She possesses numerous accomplish-

过人,音乐诗书,无不通解。昨遣某求一好儿
郎格调相称者。某具说十郎。他亦知有李十
郎名字,非常欢惬。住在胜业坊古寺曲,甫上
车门宅是也。已与他作期约。明日午时,但至
曲头觅桂子,即得矣。"

　　鲍既去,生便备行计。遂令僮秋鸿,于从
兄京兆参军尚公处假青骊驹,黄金勒。其夕,
生浣衣沐浴,修饰容仪,喜跃交并,通夕不寐。
迟明,巾帻,引镜自照,惟惧不谐也。徘徊之
间,至于亭午。遂命驾疾驱,直抵胜业。至约
之所,果见青衣立候,迎问曰:"莫是李十郎
否?"即下马,令牵入屋底,急急锁门。见鲍果
从内出来,遥笑曰:"何等儿郎,造次入此?"生
调诮未毕,引入中门。庭间有四樱桃树;西北

ments, being a poet as well as a musician, and is intellectually highly qualified. I have been commissioned by her mother yesterday to find a suitable mate for her, and I immediately mentioned your name. She had also heard of you as the famous romantic Master Li, the Tenth Favourite Son of the Li family, and was very much pleased with my suggestion. She lives in the house with wide portals to the south of the Old Temple in Sheng Yie Street. I have arranged a meeting for tomorrow noon: you can easily find the house, because a servant-maid will watch for your arrival."

After the departure of the caller, the young gallant made careful preparations for the coming interview. He sent his page to borrow from his cousin Shang, who was on the staff of the Metropolitan Garrison Headquarters, a coal-black pony equipped with a gold bit, and that night he bathed and completed his coiffure, being so exhilarated that he could not sleep a wink. As so as it was dawn he tried on his most becoming hat and gown, looking repeatedly in the mirror to see if all was in order and he was appearing at his best. He walked nervously about in the courtyard, waiting for the arrival of the hour of departure. Then he mounted his steed and galloped rapidly to the appointed spot.

A girl in black stood at the gate. "Are you Master Li the Tenth?" she queried, and led him inside the premises, locking the gate. Mrs. Bao was the first to appear.

"How dare you, stranger, invade these sacred precincts?" she chided him smilingly.

He was conducted to the second gate, where he saw before him a courtyard with four cherry trees, in the north-west corner of which hung a cage with a parrot therein.

悬一鹦鹉笼,见生入来,即语曰:"有人入来,急
下帘者!"生本性雅淡,心犹疑惧,忽见鸟语,愕
然不敢进。逡巡,鲍引净持下阶相迎,延入对
坐。年可四十余,绰约多姿,谈笑甚媚。因谓
生曰:"素闻十郎才调风流,今又见仪容雅秀,
名下固无虚士。某有一女子,虽拙教训,颜色
不致丑陋,得配君子,颇为相宜。频见鲍十一
娘说意旨,今亦便令承奉箕帚。"生谢曰:"鄙拙
庸愚,不意顾盼,倘垂采录,生死为荣。"遂命酒
馔,即令小玉自堂东阁子中而出。生即拜迎。
但觉一室之中,若琼林玉树,互相照曜,转盼精
彩射人。既而遂坐母侧。母谓曰:"汝尝爱念

"Guest has come. Raise the curtain!" cackled the parrot.

By nature timid and retiring, and feeling somewhat nervous, Li was so taken by surprise when he heard the words of the parrot, that he dared not take a step further. The girl's mother now stepped down from the terrace to welcome him and invite him inside. She was just turned forty, still an attractive woman, and showed herself a charming talker.

"I have heard a great deal of your scholarly attainments and romantic personality," she declared cordially, "and now I perceive that you are also very handsome — indeed, you do not belie your reputation. My daughter, while not highly educated, is far from being a homely person, and would really make a suitable companion for you. Mrs. Bao has transmitted to me your proposal for my daughter's hand, and I am quite ready to order her to wait on you as her lord and master."

"I am an ignorant and mediocre person, unworthy of your kind notice," politely responded the young man, "and I feel highly honoured now and hereafter to receive such a kind welcome from you, Madame."

Drink and food was then brought to celebrate the occasion, and Miss Jade was summoned to meet the visitor. She entered from an adjoining chamber on the east side of the reception room. Master Li bowed profoundly to her. The two of them made an exceedingly handsome pair, like two matching pieces of beautiful art, diffusing radiance at each other and at the others in the room. She took a seat by the side of her mother.

The mother turned to the daughter: "You love to repeat the lines:

'开帘风动竹,疑是故人来。'即此十郎诗也。尔终日吟想,何如一见。"玉乃低鬟微笑,细语曰:"见面不如闻名。才子岂能无貌?"生遂连起拜曰:"小娘子爱才,鄙夫重色。两好相映,才貌相兼。"母女相顾而笑,遂举酒数巡。生起,请玉唱歌。初不肯,母固强之。发声清亮,曲度精奇。酒阑,及暝,鲍引生就西院憩息。闲庭邃宇,帘幕甚华。鲍令侍儿桂子、浣沙与生脱靴解带。须臾,玉至,言叙温和,辞气宛媚。解罗衣之际,态有余妍,低帏昵枕,极其欢爱。生自以为巫山洛浦不过也。中宵之夜,玉忽流涕观生曰:"妾本倡家,自知非匹。今以色

*Pushing aside the curtain I note the bamboos
waving in the breeze;
Methought it a harbinger of the arrival of a dear
friend!*

"These lines, my dear, were composed by our friend Master Li. Is not his actual presence here today more interesting to you than mere recitation of his poetry?"

"What I have heard of him is really enough to make me enchanted," she lowered her head and replied in a soft voice. "Seeing him or not does not make much difference, for how can a talented scholar lack good looks?"

"You love masculine talent and I adore female beauty," declared gallantly the handsome suitor, rising from his seat and making a bow before the girl, "we thus complement each other in our ideals."

Mother and daughter smiled understandingly at each other at this gracious compliment. After several rounds of wine, Master Li arose and requested Miss Jade to favour him with a song. She modestly declined, but when her mother insisted, she complied. She possessed a rich and clear voice and the tune sounded unusually melodious.

The merry gathering lasted till evening, when Wrs. Bao conducted the young scholar to his quarters in the west courtyard, where he found the rooms quiet but elegantly furnished. Two young maids waited on him, assisting him to disrobe and retire for the night. Miss Jade did not keep him long waiting. She showed herself to be gentle and affectionate and tried her best to please him. She became his mistress that night and they were very happy together.

But in the middle of the night she commenced to weep. "I

爱,托其仁贤。但虑一旦色衰,恩移情替,使女萝无托,秋扇见捐。极欢之际,不觉悲至。"生闻之,不胜感叹。乃引臂替枕,徐谓玉曰:"平生志愿,今日获从,粉骨碎身,誓不相舍。夫人何发此言!请以素缣,著之盟约。"玉因收泪,命侍儿樱桃褰幄执烛,授生笔研。玉管弦之暇,雅好诗书,筐箱笔研,皆王家之旧物。遂取绣囊,出越姬乌丝栏素缣三尺以授生。生素多才思,援笔成章,引谕山河,指诚日月,句句恳切,闻之动人。染毕,命藏于宝箧之内。自尔婉娈相得,若翡翠之在云路也。如此二岁,日

am," she avowed to her lover, "but a common girl and I realize that I am socially not your equal. You love me for my looks, but I fear that as my beauty fades, so, too, will your sentiments fade, so that I shall resemble a vine with nothing to cling to, or like a fan that is abandoned with the passage of summer. In my hour of supreme bliss, I am overwhelmed by dark foreboding."

He was much agitated by her frank statement of her tragic presentiment.

"I have found my ideal love," he said to comfort her, using his arm to serve as her pillow. "I swear solemnly never to forsake you. If I do, may my bones by reduced to ashes and my body be broken into a thousand pieces. Why do you talk to me in the way you have done? Let me have a piece of white silk and I'll write down in ink what I have just sworn."

Cherry, the maidservant, was summoned, and she brought a yard of white satin, together with a writing brush and a stone inkslab. The elegant implements for writing came originally from her father, the Prince, Jade was literarily inclined, always fond of books, and the collection she owned also came from her father.

In the bright candlelight the scholar-lover composed and penned an original statement, in which he called on the mountains and the rivers, and the sun and the moon to bear witness to his eternal fidelity to his lady love. Every word and every sentence bore the imprint of his profound affection for and attachment to Jade, and when she eagerly read it, she sighed with great contentment. The piece of precious silk was then carefully locked away in her jewel-box.

Like a couple of love-birds, they spent happily two years

夜相从。

　　其后年春,生以书判拔萃登科,授郑县主簿。至四月,将之官,便拜庆于东洛。长安亲戚,多就筵饯。时春物尚余,夏景初丽,酒阑宾散,离思萦怀。玉谓生曰:"以君才地名声,人多景慕,愿结婚媾,固亦众矣。况堂有严亲,室无冢妇,君之此去,必就佳姻。盟约之言,徒虚语耳。然妾有短愿,欲辄指陈。永委君心,复能听否?"生惊怪曰:"有何罪过,忽发此辞? 试说所言,必当敬奉。"玉曰:"妾年始十八,君才二十有二,迨君壮室之秋,犹有八岁。一生欢爱,愿毕此期。然后妙选高门,以谐秦晋,亦未

together, hardly ever separated from each other, be it day or night. In the spring of the third year Mr. Li passed the civil service examination, and was appointed Clerk of the Zheng County, and in the fourth moon he prepared to proceed to his post. A dinner was held to celebrate the occasion, and many local friends and acquaintances made it a point to be present. It was near the end of spring and the beginning of summer, and Nature was at its best. When the wine was finished and the guests had said their adieus, the young couple were left to themselves.

"You are admired by the whole world," said Jade sadly to her sweetheart, "for your talent, your social position and your literary renown, and many a father would be proud to have you as son-in-law. Your beloved parents await keenly your return, and as there is no daughter-in-law to assist in the management of the household, you will surely get married when you are back at home. As to the troth exchanged between us and your solemn oaths, they are but vain and empty words. But I have just one tiny wish to make known to you, and in view of the deep and genuine affection I have for you, you will perhaps be willing to listen."

"In what way have I shown myself remiss that you address yourself thus to me?" cried Master Li, much taken aback and honestly pained. "I'll gladly listen to anything you desire to say to me."

"I am eighteen years of age," she began, "and you are twenty-two: there remain still eight years to elapse before you reach the traditional age of marriage. Let us two enjoy to the full our blissful love in this period: it will not be too late then for you to contract your marriage with some lady of

为晚。妾便舍弃人事，剪发披缁，夙昔之愿，于此足矣。"生且愧且感，不觉涕流。因谓玉曰："皎日之誓，死生以之，与卿偕老，犹恐未惬素志，岂敢辄有二三。固请不疑，但端居相待。至八月，必当却到华州，寻使奉迎，相见非远。"更数日，生遂诀别东去。

到任旬日，求假往东都觐亲。未至家日，太夫人已与商量表妹卢氏，言约已定。太夫人素严毅，生逡巡不敢辞让，遂就礼谢，便有近斯。卢亦甲族也，嫁女子于他门，聘财必以百万为约，不满此数，义在不行。生家素贫，事须

quality. As for me, I will shave off my hair and don the costume of a nun for the rest of my days, thus consummating happily my original vow."

"The oath I swore to the celestial bodies," he exclaimed, tears flowing down his cheeks, "I will fulfil were it to cost my life. How can I possibly think of other loves, when the good fortune has been granted me to satisfy my longing for you and to grow old with you alone? Let not your heart doubt for an instant my eternal constancy. Stay here and wait patiently. By the eighth moon I shall surely arrive at Huazhou, when I will send my people for you. It will not be long before we shall be again in each other's arms."

In a few days he left eastward for his post, and after a fortnight there he asked for leave to visit his parents in Luoyang, the ancient East Capital.

He had been home for little more than a week, when his mother informed him of a match which she had arranged between him and his cousin Miss Lu. As the old lady was very punctilious and conservative in such matters, he hesitated to express any objection, still less opposition, but was on the contrary constrained to thank her for the matrimonial arrangements she had completed for him. The wedding, she said, would take place at an early date.

Now the Lu family belonged to the aristocracy, and when marrying away one of its daughters demanded always an enormous sum as settlement from the groom or his family. If this sum was not forthcoming, the wedding would be indefinitely postponed. As the Li family was not wealthy, Li Yi was obliged to raise the wedding gift to the bride by loans from friends and relatives. Using this as a pretext, he trav-

求贷,便托假故,远投亲知,涉历江淮,自秋及夏。生自以孤负盟约,大惩回期。寂不知闻,欲断其望。遥托亲故,不遣漏言。

玉自生逾期,数访音信。虚词诡说,日日不同。博求师巫,遍询卜筮,怀忧抱恨,周岁有余,羸卧空闺,遂成沈疾。虽生之书题竟绝,而玉之想望不移,赂遗亲知,使通消息。寻求既切,资用屡空,往往私令侍婢潜卖箧中服玩之物,多托于西市寄附铺侯景先家货卖。曾令侍婢浣沙将紫玉钗一只,诣景先家货之。路逢内作老玉工,见浣沙所执,前来认之曰:"此钗,吾所作也。昔霍王小女将欲上鬟,令我作此,酬我万钱。我尝不忘。汝是何人,从何而得?"浣

elled further eastward, then southward, from the autumn till the next summer.

Realizing now that he had violated his oath to Jade and broken his promise to meet her soon, Li decided not even to correspond with her, so as to put an end once and for all to her hopes, and, moreover, cowardly requested his friends and acquaintances to keep everything about his doings secret from her.

Poor Jade did her best to obtain news of her lover after he had failed to fulfil his promise. The little she succeeded in discovering would sometimes prove later to be false, or else the information would be contradictory. She consulted all kinds of oracles and fortune-tellers without success, and finally after a year of sorrow and disappointments she fell desperately ill, becoming a confirmed invalid confined to her bedroom. Though no letter ever arrived from her former lover, her hope of seeing him again never faded. She cajoled and bribed his friends to assist her in retracing him, so that she had to spend a large part of her resources. Repeatedly she sent her maids with jewellery and ornaments for sale to a second-hand shop kept by a man by the name of Hou. She was the lucky owner of a valuable hair ornament of purple jade, which on the way to the shop was seen by a court jeweller.

"Why," he exclaimed with surprise, "that piece of jade is of my handiwork: when the youngest daughter of Prince Huo was to put up her hair, His Highness ordered me to make the pin, and gave me ten thousand copper cash for it. I remember the incident distinctly. Who are you and where did you get it?"

沙曰："我小娘子，即霍王女也。家事破散，失身于人。夫婿昨向东都，更无消息。悒怏成疾，今欲二年。令我卖此，赂遗于人，使求音信。"玉工凄然下泣曰："贵人男女，失机落节，一至于此。我残年向尽，见此盛衰，不胜伤感。"遂引至延先公主宅，具言前事。公主亦为之悲叹良久，给钱十二万焉。

时生所定卢氏女在长安，生既毕于聘财，还归郑县。其年腊月，又请假入城就亲。潜卜静居，不令人知。有明经崔允明者，生之中表弟也。性甚长厚，昔岁常与生同欢于郑氏之室，杯盘笑语，曾不相同。每得生信，必诚告于玉。玉常以薪刍衣服，资给于崔。崔颇感之。年既至，崔具以诚告玉。玉恨叹曰："天下岂有是事乎！"遍请亲朋，多方召致。生自以愆期负约，又知玉疾候沈绵，惭耻忍割，终不肯往。晨

"My mistress," replied the maid with some hesitation, "is that lady."

She related the story of how the daughter of the Prince had been seduced and abandoned by her lover for nearly two years, and how she was trying to raise some money so as to get news of his whereabouts. The jeweller felt much saddened by the story and took the girl to the Palace of Princess Yan Xian, who, sympathizing with the unhappy lot of Miss Jade, offered to buy the pin at ten times the original price.

At this time Miss Lu, the future bride of Li Yi, was also residing at Changan. Li, having succeeded in raising the fund for his wedding, returned to his post, and in the twelfth moon he asked for leave to get married. Proceeding secretly to Changan, he rented a house in a quiet neighbourhood, not letting anyone know of his presence.

However, he had in the city a cousin by the name of Cui, a master of arts and a highly honourable man, who used to drink with him at Jade's home and have merry times with him. Whenever he received any letter from Li, he would honestly transmit the content to Jade, who reciprocated by sending him gifts of fuel and clothes, for which Cui was exceedingly grateful. When Li secretly came to Changan for his marriage, Cui broke the news to her.

"Can such dishonourable conduct be possible?" she cried, her grief mixed with anger.

She earnestly requested his friends to persuade him to call at her house, but he, ashamed of having broken his promise and knowing that she was ill and almost on the verge of death, hardened his heart and refused to see his former sweetheart. He went everywhere, leaving the house early in

山暮归，欲以回避。玉日夜涕泣，都忘寝食，期
一相见，竟无因由。冤愤益深，委顿床枕。自
是长安中稍有知者。风流之士，共感玉之多
情；豪侠之伦，皆怒生之薄行。

　　时已三月，人多春游。生与同辈五六人诣
崇敬寺玩牡丹花，步于西廊，递吟诗句。有京
兆韦夏卿者，生之密友，时亦同行。谓生曰：
"风光甚丽，草木荣华。伤哉郑卿，衔冤空室！
足下终能弃置，实是忍人。丈夫之心，不宜如
此。足下宜为思之！"叹让之际，忽有一豪士，
衣轻黄纻衫，挟弓弹，丰神隽美，衣服轻华，唯
有一剪头胡雏从后，潜行而听之。俄而前揖生
曰："公非李十郎者乎？某族本山东，姻连外
戚。虽乏文藻，心尝乐贤。仰公声华，常思觏

the morning and returning late at night, but he refused to call on her, while she wept bitterly at home, refraining from food and sleep, but hoping against hope for at least an interview. Her illness became graver with each passing day.

The story of Li's scandalous treatment of his mistress became widely known among the literary and romantic circles of Changan. One and all sympathized with and lauded Miss Jade for her deep attachment to her lover and condemned Li for his heartlessness.

By then it was in the third moon, and people went out to enjoy the splendid spring weather. Li and half a dozen of his boon companions made a visit to the Chong Jing Temple to inspect the celebrated peonies, strolling in the gardens and composing poems to commemorate the occasion.

"In this beautiful weather and with Nature at her best," observed his good friend Wei Xiaqing, "it is nothing less than tragic that Miss Jade should be confined alone to her room, bearing her heavy grief. You must have a heart of stone to abandon her without any feeling of regret, and it is hardly manly on your part to act like this. I urge you to reconsider your attitude."

While the two friends were thus conversing, a stranger wearing a yellow robe and carrying a cross bow accosted them. He had striking features and was elegantly dressed, being accompanied by a Central Asian boy. He bowed to young Li and enquired if he was the well-known Master Li the Tenth.

"I am from Shandong," he explained, "and I am related to the royal family. Although I myself am no scholar, I admire learning, and having heard so much of your brilliant at-

止。今日幸会，得睹清扬。某之敝居，去此不
远，亦有声乐，足以娱情。妖姬八九人，骏马十
数匹，唯公所欲。但愿一过。"生之侪辈，共聆
斯语，更相叹美。因与豪士策马同行，疾转数
坊，遂至胜业。生以近郑之所止，意不欲过，便
托事故，欲回马首。豪士曰："敝居咫尺，忍相
弃乎？"乃挽挟其马，牵引而行。迁延之间，已
及郑曲。生神情恍惚，鞭马欲回。豪士遽命奴
仆数人，抱持而进。疾走推入车门，便令锁却，
报云："李十郎至也！"一家惊喜，声闻于外。先
此一夕，玉梦黄衫丈夫抱生来，至席，使玉脱
鞋。惊寤而告母。因自解曰："鞋者，谐也。夫
妇再合。脱者，解也。既合而解，亦当永诀。
由此征之，必遂相见，相见之后，当死矣。"凌
晨，请母梳妆。母以其久病，心意惑乱，不堪信
之。僶勉之间，强为妆梳。妆梳才毕，而生果

tainments, I am proud to make your acquaintance. My humble house is not far from here, and I can provide music to
entertain you. In the house you will also find some pretty
girls and in the stables a dozen steeds. You may have any of
these if you will honour me with your visit."

Li's friends hearing the invitation were eager to visit the
house, and mounting their ponies they galloped after their
genial host. After several turnings, the party found itself in
Sheng Yie Street and Li, realizing that they were in the vicinity of Jade's home, raised objection to proceeding any further. The stranger, saying that his house was only a few
yards away, seized the bridle of Li's mount and dragged the
animal along. In a few minutes the party arrived at Jade's
door. The heartless lover made another attempat to escape,
but the gallant stranger summoned his servants who were at
hand, and had him carried, willy-nilly, inside. As soon as
the party had entered the door was locked.

"Master Li the Tenth has come," shouted the cavalier,
and the entire Zheng household appeared in great amazement
and rapture.

Now during the preceding night Miss Jade dreamed that
her lover, borne by a yellow-robed man, paid her a visit and
on their entry the stranger asked her to remove Li's shoes. In
the morning she related the dream to her mother and inter-
preted it to herself as follows: shoes stood for harmony (The
character for "shoe" and that for "harmony" have the same
sound.) — which meant that Li was to come to her, but re-
moval meant parting for ever after the meeting. So she requested her mother to help her coiffure, which the latter did,
simply to humour her, believing that in her serious illness

至。玉沈绵日久，转侧须人。忽闻生来，欻然
自起，更衣而出，恍若有神。遂与生相见，含怒
凝视，不复有言。羸质娇姿，如不胜致，时复掩
袂，返顾李生。感物伤人，坐皆欷歔。顷之，有
酒肴数十盘，自外而来。一座惊视，遽问其故，
悉是豪士之所致也。因遂陈设，相就而坐。玉
乃侧身转面，斜视生良久，遂举杯酒，酬地曰：
"我为女子，薄命如斯。君是丈夫，负心若此。
韶颜稚齿，饮恨而终。慈母在堂，不能供养。
绮罗弦管，从此永休。征痛黄泉，皆君所致。
李君李君，今当永诀！我死之后，必为厉鬼，使
君妻妾，终日不安！"乃引左手握生臂，掷杯于
地，长恸号哭数声而绝。母乃举尸，置于生怀，

her mind was not working normally. Soon after, however, Li actually arrived together with the party.

Although much enfeebled, Miss Jade seemed suddenly to recover her strength, and as soon as the visitors were announced, she jumped up from her bed, dressed properly and went out to meet her ex-sweetheart, as if in a trance. For a while she stared at him with anger in her eyes then raised an arm to hide her face as if unable to sustain the sight of him. After a while, however, she glanced at Li from behind her sleeves, her eyes now expressing infinite sorrow and reproach. In spite of her brave front, she could not conceal from those present the ravages of her very serious malady, which only intensified their sympathy for her.

To the surprise of all, soon a magnificent repast was laid out. Inquiries elicited the information that it was provided by the same chivalrous stranger. After all had sat down, Jade, sitting sideways and gazing at her lover for a few minutes, took up her cup and poured the wine on the floor.

"I am only a woman of unhappy fate," she cried, "but you are an utterly heartless man. About to die of a broken heart in my young womanhood, I will no longer be able to support my beloved mother. Goodbye to my books and to my musical instruments! I have also to thank you, my faithless lover, for my coming suffering in purgatory. So adieu, Master Li! After my death, however, I shall become an evil spirit and return to this world to torment you and your wife, so that you will never know a day of peace and happiness."

Grasping Li's arm with her left hand, she flung her wine-cup on the floor, breaking it into a hundred pieces. She gave several wails and moans, then expired. Her mother, placing

令唤之,遂不复苏矣。生为之缟素,且夕哭泣甚哀。将葬之夕,生忽见玉缥帷之中,容貌妍丽,宛若平生。著石榴裙,紫褙裆,红绿帔子。斜身倚帷,手引绣带,顾谓生曰:"愧君相送,尚有余情。幽冥之中,能不感叹。"言毕,遂不复见。明日,葬于长安御宿原。生至墓所,尽哀而返。后月余,就礼于卢氏。伤情感物,郁郁不乐。夏五月,与卢氏偕行,归于郑县。至县旬日,生方与卢氏寝,忽帐外叱叱作声。生惊视之,则见一男子,年可二十余,姿状温美,藏身暎幔,连招卢氏。生惶遽走起,绕幔数匝,倏然不见。生自此心怀疑恶,猜忌万端,夫妻之间,无聊生矣。或有亲情,曲相劝喻。生意稍解。后旬日,生复自外归,卢氏方鼓琴于床,忽见自门抛一斑犀钿花合子,方圆一寸余,中有

the body of her daughter in Li's lap, urged him to try to revive her, but his efforts were unavailing.

Master Li went into deep mourning and showed great sorrow at Jade's death. On the eve of the interment he saw her once more appear behind the curtains which concealed the coffin: she was as beautiful as when she was alive, wearing her old skirt of the colour of pomegranate seeds, her purple jacket, and the shawl of red and green, holding in her hand the ribbons attached to her dress. She intimated to him that she appreciated his feelings in seeing her off from the world, and though now only a spirit, she still retained sentiments of regret and pity for him. Then she vanished and never appeared to him again. The following day her remains were buried in a Chang'an cemetery, Li walking behind the coffin all the way to the grave.

A month later Li married his cousin, Miss Lu, but not being able entirely to forget his previous love, he was not happy. The new couple went soon after to Li's post in Zheng County.

One night while in bed, he was suddenly awakened by a sound outside the curtains, and on looking out saw a handsome young man, beckoning to his wife from behind the window shades. Jumping out of bed, he looked for the intruder, but the latter had vanished. From that time on he suspected his wife of unfaithfulness, and a coolness arose between them. On the intervention of friends, however, he was induced to forget the incident.

About ten days later, on returning home, he found his wife playing on the lute in her boudoir, when all of a sudden someone threw into the room a small, elegant inlaid jewel-

轻绢,作同心结,坠于卢氏怀中。生开而视之,见相思子二,叩头虫一,发杀觜一,驴驹媚少许。生当时愤怒叫吼,声如豺虎,引琴撞击其妻,诘令实告。卢氏亦终不自明。尔后往往暴加捶楚,备诸毒虐,竟讼于公庭而遣之。卢氏既出,生或侍婢媵妾之属,暂同枕席,便加妒忌。或有因而杀之者。生尝游广陵,得名姬曰营十一娘者,容态润媚,生甚悦 之。每相对坐,尝谓营曰:"我尝于某处得某姬,犯某事,我以某法杀之。"日日陈说,欲令惧己,以肃清闺门。出则以浴斛覆营于床,周回封署,归必详视,然后乃开。又畜一短剑,甚利,顾谓侍婢曰:"此信州葛溪铁,唯断作罪过头!"大凡生所见妇人,辄加猜忌,至于三娶,率皆如初焉。

box, tied with a ribbon in the shape of a lover's knot. It fell into his wife's lap. Snatching it, he opened it. Inside he found love philtres and aphrodisiacs. The discovery made him violently angry. He roared like a wild beast, seized the lute and struck his wife with it, demanding an explanation of the affair, of which she herself was honestly unaware. After that incident, he assaulted her frequently, ending in their going to court and getting divorced. The handmaids and concubines who shared his bed later on fared no better at his hands, and one of them was actually killed by him in a fit of insane jealousy.

Visiting Guangling, he married a concubine by the name of Miss Ying the Eleventh, a great beauty, who became his favourite. To frighten her into good behaviour he used to relate to her the fate of some of her predecessors — where he came to know them and how he got rid of them for their misdeeds. When he was obliged to leave the house, he would cover her in bed with a bathtub, sealing the edges. When he returned he would examine minutely the seals before permitting her to leave the bed. He kept always on his person a short sharp sword, showing it often to the handmaids and boasting that it was made of the finest steel and could easily sever the head of any woman who was unfaithful to him.

During his entire life he was obsessed with jealousy and suspicions concerning the women of his household, and though he married three times, the marriages all ended in great unhappiness for him.

裴伷先别传

阙 名

工部尚书裴伷先，年十七，为太仆寺丞。伯父相国炎遇害，伷先废为民，迁岭外。

伷先素刚，痛伯父无罪，乃于朝廷上封事请见，面陈得失。天后大怒，召见，盛气以待之，谓伷先曰："汝伯父反，干国之宪，自贻伊戚，尔欲何言？"伷光对曰："臣今请为陛下计，安敢诉冤？且陛下先帝皇后，李家新妇。先帝

GOOD FORTUNE
WAITS ON COURAGE
Anonymous

Pei Youxian, the famous Minister of Public Works of the Tang Dynasty, was already at the age of seventeen Deputy Chief of the Royal Stable. When his uncle, the Prime Minister Pei Yan, though innocent of the crime with which he was charged, was beheaded, he himself was reduced to a commoner and banished beyond the frontier mountains. Now the young man possessed great moral courage, and chafing grievously under the injustice done to his uncle, presented a sealed memorial to the throne, praying to be granted an audience so as to expound the grave mistakes committed by the government.

Her Majesty the Empress-Ruler Wu, greatly angered by what she considered his youthful impertinence, summoned him to court.

"Your uncle committed high treason, thus violating the established laws of the land, and incurred due punishment," Her Majesty declared severely. "What do you, in requesting an audience, desire to say?"

"I am here not to complain against the grave miscarriage of justice in the case of my uncle," he boldly replied, "but to give counsel to Your Majesty in order to assure the safety and happiness of your own future. Your Majesty came as bride to the imperial Li family and became later empress. When His Majesty departed from this world, you succeeded

弃世，陛下临朝，为妇道者理当委任大臣，保其
宗社。东宫年长，复子明辟，以塞天人之望。
今先帝登遐未几，遽自封崇私室，立诸武为王，
诛斥李宗，自称皇帝，海内愤惋，苍生失望，臣
伯父至忠于李氏，反诬其罪，戮及子孙。陛下
为计若斯，臣深痛惜，臣望陛下复立李家社稷，
迎太子东宫。陛下高枕，诸武获全。如不纳臣
言，天下一动，大事去矣，产禄之诫，可不惧哉？
臣今为陛下计，能用臣言，犹未晚也。"天后怒

as ruler, but since you are a woman it was your duty to have nominated a minister of state to act as regent, and, when the heir apparent later reached the age of majority, to permit him to ascend the throne as emperor, thus fulfilling both the will of Heaven and the hopes of the nation.

"To the contrary, not long after the lamented decease of His Majesty you elevated the rank of your own Wu family, ennobled several of its male members as princes, banished or executed the members of the imperial Li family, and usurped the title of Empress-Ruler, thus causing deep regret and anguish to the whole nation. My uncle, who was profoundly loyal to the imperial Li family, was falsely accused of high treason, bringing death to himself and to his family. I consider such a policy on the part of Your Majesty as very unwise and deplorable. It is my humble hope that Your Majesty restore the position of the Li family, welcome the return of the heir apparent, and in acting in this manner assure yourself of peaceful repose and the members of the Wu family a secure future. Otherwise, I am afraid, the situation will become very unfavourable to Your Majesty once the whole nation is driven into some action. The rebellion of An Lu-shan and others in the past should be a warning for us, and it is not yet too late for Your Majesty to consider and accept my words of advice."

"How dare you, you impudent young man, talk to me like this?" cried the Empress-Ruler with fury, and ordered that he be dragged away for punishment.

As he was being removed, Pei turned around three times and shouted to Her Majesty: "It is not yet too late for you to accept my counsel!"

曰："何物小子，敢发此言！"命牵出。仙先犹反顾曰："陛下采臣言，实未晚。"如是者三天，后令集朝臣于朝堂，杖仙先至百，长隶灢州。仙先解衣受杖，笞至十而仙先死。数至九十八而苏，更二笞而毕。

仙先疮甚，卧驴舆中，至流所，卒不死。在南中数岁，娶流人卢氏女，生男愿，卢氏卒。仙先携愿潜归乡，岁余事发，又杖一百，配北庭。货殖五年，致资财数千万。仙先贤相之侄，往来河西，所在交二千石。北庭都护府城下有夷万帐，则降胡也。其可汗礼仙先，以女妻之。可汗唯一女，念之甚，赠仙先黄金马驼牛羊甚众。仙先因而致富，门下食客常数千人。自北庭至东京，累道置客，以取东京息耗，朝廷动静。不数日，仙先必知之。时补阙李秦授寓直

The Empress-Ruler commanded that the high officials be assembled at court, and that Pei Youxian be given a hundred lashes in their presence and then be exiled for ever to Rangzhou. Pei disrobed himself to be beaten. He fainted after receiving ten lashes, but regained consciousness at the last three strokes.

Severely injured, Pei lay in his mulecart on the way to his place of banishment in south China, but, strange to relate, survived his punishment. Living there for some years, he married a Miss Lu, the daughter of another exile, and had a son by her, whom he named Yuan. His wife dying soon after, Pei returned secretly to his native place with the child. A year after his return he was rearrested, given another hundred lashes and exiled this time to Beiting in the area of the Huns. There he engaged himself in trading and, within five years, amassed great riches. He travelled extensively in north-west China and as the nephew of a former prime minister he made many friends among the wealthy offcials.

Now there lived in some ten thousand yurts on the outskirts of Beiting a large number of the northern barbarian tribesmen, who had previously submitted to the Tang Empire. Their Khan held Pei in great esteem, finally accepting him as suitor to his only daughter. He presented Pei with gold and herds of camels, horses and cattle, so that the young man became richer than ever, supporting at times as many as several thousand retainers. He stationed his men all along the route between Beiting and the imperial capital to collect and transmit political information, so that every move at court would become known to him within a few days.

Meanwhile, a junior member of the Grand Secretariat by

中书，进封事曰："陛下自登极，诛斥李氏及诸大臣，其家人亲族流放在外。以臣所料，且数万人。如一旦同心，招集为逆，出陛下不意，臣恐社稷必危。谶曰代武者刘，夫刘者流也。陛下不杀此辈，臣恐为祸深隐。"天后纳之，夜中召入谓曰："卿名秦授，天以卿授朕也，何启予心。"即拜考功员外郎，仍知制诰，赐朱绂女妓十人，金帛称是。与谋发敕使十人于十道，安慰流者。其实赐墨敕与牧守，有流放者杀之。敕既下，佃先知之。会宾客计议，皆劝佃先入胡，佃先从之。日晚，舍于城外。束装时有铁

the name of Li Qinshou memorialized the Empress-Ruler, pointing out that since Her Majesty ascended the throne, she had executed many members of the imperial Li clan as well as loyal ministers of His Late Majesty, and had banished their relatives to the outlying provinces, to the total number of tens of thousands. If these people should unite themselves and suddenly organize a revolution, he thought, the empire would be endangered. The oracles had already proclaimed that the Liu's would replace the wu's on the throne: now the "Liu's" could as well be the exiles, since the characters for the two were pronounced exactly the same. If Her Majesty, therefore, did not anticipate this danger and exterminate them as soon as possible, he feared, a disaster was in the making.

The wicked suggestion was warmly approved by Her Majesty, who summoned Li to a midnight conference.

"You must have been sent to me by Heaven, so well do you understand the inner workings of my heart," she graciously said to him.

He was given promotion in rank, ten girl musicians, gold and many rolls of silk, and the Empress-Ruler conspired with him to send ten imperial envoys, nominally to bring messages of comfort to the exiles scattered in the ten territorial districts, but actually to transmit secret orders to the local prefects to kill them.

Pei got wind of the secret orders almost as soon as they were issued, and he called a meeting of his retainers. They were unanimous in their advice that he should seek safety in the country of the nomads, which he accepted, concealing himself that very night outside the city walls and making

骑果毅二人,勇而有力,以罪流,仙先善待之。
及行,使将马牛橐驼八十头,尽装金帛。宾客
家僮从之者三百余人,甲兵备足,曳犀超乘者
半。有千里马二,仙先与妻乘之。装毕遽发,
料天晓人觉之,已入虏境矣。既而迷失道,迟
明唯进一舍,乃驰。既明,候者言仙先走。都
护令八百骑追之,妻父可汗又令五百骑急追,
诫追者曰:"舍仙先与妻,同行者尽杀之,货财
为赏。"追者及仙先于塞,仙先勒兵与战,麾下
皆殊死战,杀追骑五百人。日昏,二将战死而
败。缚仙先及妻与橐驼,将至都护所。既至,
械击阱中,具以状闻待报,而使者至,召流人数
百皆害之,仙先以未报故免。

preparations to escape. Two brave and powerful horsemen, also exiles, who for some years had been in his service gathered together his camels, horses and oxen, some eighty in all, and loaded them with their master's gold, silks and other valuables. With the retainers, domestics and others, the cavalcade included in all more than three hundred souls; half of them mounted and well armed. Pei himself and his princess-wife rode on two of the best steeds and headed the caravan as soon as it was ready to start, believing that by dawn, when their departure would have been noted, they should be already within the nomad frontiers.

Unfortunately, they missed the trail, so that when daylight came, they had covered only the first stage of their journey. On the other hand, when the Commanding General of Beiting heard of Pei's flight, he sent eight hundred cavalrymen in pursuit, and the Khan, his father-in-law, also despatched five hundred of his horsemen to assist in the chase.

"With the exception of Pei and my daughter," ran the Khan's instructions, "you are to slay all the others. Whatever booty you secure, you may divide among yourselves."

A fierce battle ensued between the pursuers and the pursued, and as the latter fought desperately, they killed five hundred of the former. By evening, however, Pei's two brave retainers fell, and he and his wife were captured and brought back to Beiting, where they were thrown into prison. As their capture was not immediately reported, their names were not included in the list of several exiles to be executed on the arrival and at the order of the imperial envoy. So they escaped death.

Her Majesty, believing that most of the exiles had been

　　天后度流人已死，又使使者安抚流人曰：
"吾前使十道使安慰流人，何使者不晓吾意？
擅加杀害，深为酷暴。"其辄杀流人使者，并所
在锁项，将至害流人处斩之，以快亡魂。诸流
人未死，或他事系者，兼家口放还，由是仙先得
免，乃归乡里。

　　及唐室再造，宥裴炎，赠以益州大都督，求
其后。仙先乃出，授詹事丞，岁中四迁，遂至秦
州都督，再节制桂广，一任幽州帅，四为执金
吾，一兼御史大夫太原京兆尹太府卿。凡任三
品官，向四十政，所在有声绩，号称名臣，后为
工部尚书东京留守。薨，寿八十六。

killed, now sent another batch of envoys to appease the remaining ones. These were told that the former envoys had misunderstood their instructions and had cruelly and wrongfully executed many exiles. To expiate their crime and avenge the dead, the unlucky envoys were loaded with chains and transported to the places of their alleged misdeed to be beheaded! As evidence of imperial clemency, the edict continued, the surviving and free exiles, as well as those still in prison, were pardoned and permitted to return to their homes. Thus Pei was freed and safely returned to his native place.

Subsequently, when the imperial Li family was restored to power, the new emperor pardoned posthumously the former Prime Minister Pei Yan and conferred on him the honorific title of Governor-General of Yizhow. As a member of the Pei family, Youxian was also restored to his official rank. In the course of one year he received four promotions, and then became Governor of Qinzhou, that of Guizhou and Guangxi, and Commander of the Youzhou Garrison. Later he was appointed to high posts in the capital, becoming renowned as a distinguished statesman and ending his career as Minister of Public Works. He died when he was eighty-six years of age.

枕中记

李泌

开元十九年，道者吕翁经邯郸道上，邸舍中设榻施席，担囊而坐。俄有邑中少年卢生，衣短褐，乘青驹，将适于田，亦止邸中，与翁接席，言笑殊畅。久之，卢生顾其衣装敝褒，乃叹曰："大丈夫生世不谐，而困如是乎！"翁曰："观子肤极腴，体胖无恙，谈谐方适，而叹其困者何也？"生曰："吾此苟生耳，何适之为！"翁曰："此而不适，于何为适？"生曰："当建功树名，出将

A DREAM AND ITS LESSON
Li Mi

In the nineteenth year of the reign of Kai Yuan in the Tang Dynasty, an old Taoist, on his journey to Handan, arrived at a small inn. Spreading a mat on the *kang*, he unburdened himself of the bag from his shoulder and sat down. A young man by the name of Lu, wearing a short fur jacket and riding a pony, being on his way to tend his farm, also stopped at the inn for a brief rest. He made the acquaintance of the old Taoist and the two chatted pleasantly for some time.

Looking at his own shabby attire, the young man sighed in the middle of the conversation.

"It is a shame," he complained, "that a man like me should have no luck in life and be indigent like this."

"Your face has a good colour, you seem to be well nourished and in excellent health, and you converse pleasantly, why should you sigh and complain of your hard luck?" rejoined the old man.

"I am barely hanging on to life," was the moody reply, "and there is practically no happiness to speak of."

"If such as you are discontented with life," observed the Taoist, "with what should one then be satisfied?"

"A man should have the opportunity to render distinguished service to his country and acquire wide renown, either as a general or as a minister of state," claimed the

入相,列鼎而食,选声而听。使族益茂而家用
肥,然后可以言其适。吾志于学而游于艺,自
惟当年朱紫可拾。今已过壮室,犹勤田亩,非
困而何?"言讫,目昏思寐。

　　是时主人蒸黄粱为馔,翁乃探囊中枕以授
之曰:"子枕此,当令子荣适如志。"其枕瓷,而
窍其两端。生俯首就之。寐中,见其窍大而
明,若可处,举身而入,遂至其家。娶清河崔氏
女,女容甚丽,而产甚殷。由是衣裘服御,日以

young man. "He would then be wined and dined and enter-tained with music of his choice, his family and relations would become prosperous and influential, and he would be able to spend money freely in his household expenditures. Then and then only may one admit that he is contented. In my case I have devoted my time and energy to learning and I am also proficient in many arts. I believed at one time that I could pass with ease the imperial examinations and receive deservedly high official appointments. Today I am no longer young, and yet I have to toil in the fields from morning to night. If this is not misfortune, then I do not know what is."

When he had finished his discourse, he was becoming somewhat drowsy and felt like taking a nap. As the innkeep-er was then engaged in cooking some millet for his meal, the old Taoist reached for his bag and took from it a pillow which he handed to the young man.

"Put this pillow under your head," he said, "it will bring you all that you yearn for — honours, fame, wealth and what not."

The pillow made of porcelain was hollow and the two ends were open. Lu placed his head on it and soon fell sound asleep.

In his dream he saw that the apertures of the pillow were enlarging to a size that would admit his body, and it was bright inside. Boldly he entered and soon found himself back at home. Before long a marriage was arranged between him and a Miss Cui of Qinghe, a wealthy and beautiful heiress, and from that time on he lived luxuriously, wearing rich and soft furs and going about in handsome equipages.

华侈。明年,举进士,登甲科,解褐授校书郎。应制举,授渭南县尉,迁监察御史起居舍人,为制诰。三年即真,出典同州,寻转陕州。生好土功,自陕西开河八十里,以济不通,邦人赖之,立碑颂德。迁汴州岭南道采访使,入京为京兆尹。是时神武皇帝方事夷狄,吐蕃新诺罗龙莽布攻陷瓜沙,节度使王君㚟新被败死,河湟震恐。帝思将帅之任,遂除生御史中丞河西陇右节度使。大破戎虏,斩首七千级,开地九百里,筑三大城以防要害,北边赖之,以石纪功焉。

　　归朝策勋,恩礼极崇。转御史大夫吏部侍

The following year he obtained the doctorate at the metropolitan examination and was appointed Imperial Compiler. Passing with flying colours the civil service test he was nominated Magistrate of the Weinan County, and breveted soon after as Censor, stepping into that post within three years. Rapid promotions followed, for he became Prefect of Tongzhou, and was subsequently transferred to Shanzhou.

Now Lu was keen on engineering projects and during his stay at Shanzhou constructed a canal eighty *li* long, thus facilitating irrigation and transportation in that region. To commemorate this valuable service to the locality, the people erected honorific stone tablets. After occupying the higher post of Intendant of Bianzhou, he was further honoured with the appointment of Governor of the Metropolitan District.

At the time the emperor was engaged in conflicts with the nomadic tribes in the north-west. The Khan of the Turfans had attacked and captured two important Chinese cities, killing the Chinese Commanding General Wang. The vast north-western territory being threatened with invasion, His Majesty sought for a capable military leader. The choice fell on Governor Lu, who smashed the barbarian onslaught, killed some seven thousand enemy troops, brought a territory of several thousand square *li* under imperial rule and constructed three big fortified cities as key points in this important strategical area. Thus the empire's frontiers on the north were made invulnerable, and Lu's exploits were engraved on stone to immortalize his name.

On his triumphant return to the capital he was showered with honours and received the appointment of Censor and Vice-Minister of Civil Service. Enjoying now high prestige

郎,物望清重,群情翕习,大为当时宰相所忌,以飞语中之,贬端州刺史,三年征还。除户部尚书,未几拜中书侍郎同中书门下平章事,与萧令嵩裴侍中光庭同掌大政十年。嘉谋密命,一日三接,献替启沃,号为贤相。同列者害之,遂诬与边将交结,所图不轨,下狱。府吏引徒至其门,追之甚急,生惶骇不测,泣谓妻子曰:"吾家本山东,良田数顷,足以御寒馁,何苦求禄而今及此! 思复衣短裘,乘青驹,行邯郸道中,不可得也。"引刀欲自裁,其妻救之得免。共罪者皆死,生独有中人保护,得减死论。出

and becoming an idol of the people, he incurred the jealousy of the Prime Minister, who tried his best by spreading malicious rumours to destroy the national hero. Lu was, as a consequence, demoted to Prefect of Duanzhou, and returned to the capital only after serving in the province for three years.

However, this time he was promoted to be Minister of Finance, later became Imperial Secretary, and, together with two others, was in control of state affairs for a period of ten years. He was consulted as often as three times a day by His Majesty on imperial problems, and his ripe experience and profound grasp of statecraft earned for him the reputation of being a very wise premier.

Once more his colleagues intrigued and plotted against him, accusing him of maintaining secret and improper relations with frontier military officers with a view to high treason. He was condemned to imprisonment. The police came to his house to arrest him. He was so frightened at the thought of the death penalty that he confessed his innermost thoughts to his wife.

"My family came originally from Shandong," he said, "we owned several hundred *mu* of fertile land, which was sufficient to feed and clothe us comfortably. Why did I then foolishly seek for official honours, only to arrive at such a pass? At this moment it is not even possible for me to wear my short fur jacket and, mounting my pony, gallop gaily on the road to Handan."

He took a knife to commit suicide by cutting his throat but was prevented from killing himself by his wife. In the end, while all his fellow accused were beheaded, he was spared

授骦牧。

　　数岁，帝知其冤，复起为中书令，封赵国公。恩旨殊渥，备极一时。生有五子，傅偒俭位倚，傅为考功员外，俭为侍御史，位为太常丞，偒万年尉，季子倚最贤，年二十四为右补阙。其姻媾皆天下族望，有孙十余人。凡两窜岭表，再登台铉，出入中外，回翔台阁。三十余年间，崇盛赫奕，一时无比。末节颇奢荡，好逸乐，后庭声色皆第一。前后赐良田甲第，佳人名马，不可胜数。后年渐老，屡乞骸骨不许。及病，中人候望，接踵于路，名医上药毕至焉。将终，上疏曰："臣本山东书生，以田圃为娱，偶逢圣运，得列官序，过蒙荣奖，特受鸿私，出拥

his life through friendly intervention, and later appointed Magistrate of Huan.

A few years afterwards His Majesty, realizing that Lu had been a victim of injustice, recalled him to the capital and restored him to the post of Imperial Secretary, besides ennobling him as the Duke of Zhao. Once more he basked in imperial favour and was the envy of all officialdom. All his five sons held fat posts under the government, while his relatives by marriage belonged all to illustrious families of the empire. He was, moreover, the proud grandfather of more than a dozen boys.

Twice during his career he was banished to the provinces and twice he returned to power. He was a prominent figure in and out of the capital and he played a preponderating role around the throne. For thirty years he enjoyed to the full both renown and authority, and no other minister of state could boast of such a brilliant career.

In his later years he indulged freely in luxury and extravagance, and spent much time in his harem. The emperor bestowed on him huge estates and mansions, as well as beautiful women and noble horses. As he aged, he prayed to the emperor to be relieved of his important posts, but met only with refusals. Finally, he fell desperately ill. Medicines came to him from the imperial pharmacy. Noted physicians ministered to him. Visitors to his palace to enquire after his health arrived in a veritable procession. On his deathbed he prepared his last memorial to the throne.

"Your liege servant," he modestly stated, "started out in life as a humble scholar of Shandong, who occupied himself with farming and gardening, but through imperial patronage

旄钺，入昇鼎辅，周旋中外。绵历岁年，有忝恩造，无裨圣化。负乘致寇，履薄临兢，日极一日，不知老之将至。今年逾八十，位历三公，钟漏并歇，筋骸俱弊，弥留沈困，殆将溘尽。顾无诚效，上答休明，空负深恩，永辞圣代，无任感恋之至，谨奉表称谢以闻。"诏曰："卿以俊德，作朕元辅，出雄藩垣，入赞缉熙，昇平二纪，实卿是赖。比因疾累，日谓痊除，岂遽沈顿。良

was enabled to enter the government service. He was promoted beyond his deserts and has received many honours and awards from the throne. Proceeding to the frontiers on a military mission, he was escorted by a forest of banners, and serving in the capital he was permitted to stand close to the Imperial Presence, thus basking in the imperial sunshine without making appreciable contribution to the Sacred Rule. Nevertheless, your servant battled on horseback not unsuccessfully against the barbarian invader, proceeding in his strategy with a prudence as if he were walking on thin ice over deep waters.

"One day thus followed another without your liege's noticing the rapid approach of old age: today he is over eighty, having attained one of the three highest posts in the government. The sands of his life are fast running out, and his old bones and shrivelled muscles can no longer stand the strain of work. He is confined to his bed breathing his last, feeling that he has reached the end of his efforts. Unable to repay any further his indebtedness to His Gracious Majesty, he craves on his knees to bid eternal and loving farewell to his Imperial Master and Sovereign."

His Majesty the Emperor deigned to grant a gracious rescript:

"You have with your eminent talent and virtues nobly supported us in the government of the empire. Out on the distant frontiers you played the part of an impregnable rampart, while in the capital you contributed your invaluable counsel for promoting the peace and prosperity of the land. The well-being and security of the empire during a period of more than a score of years have been due to your wise statesman-

深悯默，今遣骠骑大将军高力士，就第候省，其勉加针灸，为朕自爱，燕冀无妄，期于有喜。"其夕卒。

卢生欠伸而寤，见方偃於邸中，顾吕翁在旁，主人蒸黄梁尚未熟。触类如故，蹶然而兴曰："岂其梦寐耶?"翁笑谓曰："人世之事，亦犹是矣。"生怃然良久，谢曰："夫宠辱之数，得丧之理，生死之情，尽知之矣。此先生所以窒吾欲也，敢不受教?"再拜而去。

ship. When we heard of your illness, we had hoped that you would soon recover, but now we learn to our profound sorrow of its gravity. We are sending Field Marshal Gao to pay you a visit and enquire after your condition. We trust that for our sake you will continue to take good care of yourself, follow faithfully the advice of the physicians, and while placing no reliance on false hopes, await patiently a happy issue to the present struggle."

That night the illustrious statesman died.

Now our young man Lu gave a yawn and awoke, finding himself lying in the inn. The old Taoist was sitting by his side, the millet which the innkeeper was cooking over the fire was not quite ready, and everything else in the room remained the same as before. He jumped up with a start.

"Was all this merely a dream?" he asked.

"All human affairs are like this," replied the old man with a laugh.

For a long while the young man cogitated. Finally he spoke to the old Taoist.

"I thank you, sir, for the wonderful experience," he said slowly. "I fully grasp the meaning now of the cycle of honour and disgrace, of the principle of seeming loss and gain, and of life and death. You have taught me an invaluable lesson as regards personal ambitions, and I remain always your grateful and obedient pupil."

He bowed profoundly and went to tend his farm.

采药民

阙 名

唐高宗显庆中,有蜀郡青城民,不得姓名,尝采药于青城山下,遇一大薯药,劚之。深数丈,其根渐大如瓮。此人劚之不已,渐深五六丈,而地陷不止。至十丈余,此人堕中,无由而出。仰视穴口,大如星焉,分必死矣。

忽旁见一穴,既入,稍大,渐渐匍匐,可数十步。前视如有明状,寻之而行。一里余,此穴渐高,绕穴行可一里许。乃出一洞口,洞上有水,阔数十步。岸上见有数十人家,村落桑柘,花物草木,如二三月中。有人男女衣服,不似今人。耕夫钓童,往往相遇。一人惊问得来

THE HERBALIST'S STRANGE ADVENTURE
Anonymous

During the reign of Xian Qing in the Tang Dynasty there lived in Qingcheng in the province of Sichuan a man whose name is not remembered. When seeking medicinal herbs at the foot of a hill in the outskirts, he discovered a huge potato plant. He commenced to dig. Reaching a depth of thirty feet he found one of the tubers which was of the size of a water jar. He continued excavating till he attained the depth of about sixty feet, when the soil began to crumble, and he found himself in a pit so deep that he could not climb out. He looked upward and the mouth of the pit appeared like a star, causing him to dread that he would surely be buried alive.

To his surprise and joy, however, he found on one side of the pit a cavity which increased in size the further he crawled, and in the distance he could see a dim light. After a quarter of a mile the hole increased in height and width till it ended in a large cavern.

Outside the cavern a stretch of water separated him from the land on the other side, whereon were a score of farmhouses, looking like a village, with mulberry trees and plants and flowers. It seemed to be springtime, in the second or third moon, and men and women were walking about with dresses unlike those of his time. Some were evidently tillers of the soil, while others were lads going to fish.

之由，遂告所以。乃将小舠子渡之。民告之
曰："不食已经三日矣。"遂食以胡麻饭柏子汤
诸蔬，止可数日，此民觉身渐轻，问其主人，此
是何所，兼求还蜀之路。其人相与笑曰："汝世
人，不知此仙境。汝得至此，当是合有仙分。
可且留此，吾当引汝谒玉皇。"又其中相呼云：
"明日上巳也，可往朝谒。"

　　遂将此人往，其民或乘云气，或驾龙鹤，此
人亦在云中徒步。须臾至一城，皆金玉为饰，
其中宫阙，皆是金宝。诸人皆以次入谒，独留
此人于宫门外。门侧有一大牛，赤色，形状甚
异，闭目吐涎沫。主人令此民礼拜其牛，求乞
仙道，如牛吐宝物，即便吞之。此民如言拜乞，
少顷此牛吐一赤珠，大逾径寸，民方欲捧接，

They were amazed to see him and questioned him on how he got there. After hearing his story, they ferried him across in a small boat, when he told them that he had not eaten for three days. They fed him with gruel made with the seed of the sesame accompanied by a vegetable soup, and, after staying for a few days, he noticed that he had become much lighter in weight.

He asked his hosts where he was and wanted to know how to return home. They all laughed.

"You are a man of the earth, and so you have no idea of Heaven," they cried. "The fact that you are here, however, seems to prove that you have a divine spark. Remain with us a while, and we'll present you to the Emperor of Heaven."

"Tomorrow is Court Day," one of them remarked. "You can attend the audience."

The next day the man went with his friends to the palace. On the way they met many others bound for the same destination, some riding on dragons and storks, others being transported by clouds. Walking themselves on the clouds they arrived at a city of gold and jade, with palaces and halls magnificently adorned with precious stones.

The others went into the audience hall according to their turn, leaving him with his host at the gate, by the side whereof stood a large red bull of very strange appearance, with eyes closed and saliva dripping from its mouth. His host directed him to render honour to the beast and to pray to it to show him the way to the Truth. If the beast should let drop from its mouth any precious jewel, he should grasp it with alacrity and swallow it at once.

The man did as instructed. In a moment the bull let drop a

忽有一赤衣童子拾之而去。民再求，得青珠，又为青衣童子所取。又有黑者白者，皆有童子夺之。民遂急以手捧牛口，须臾得黑珠，遽自吞之，黑衣童子至，无所见而空去。主人遂引谒玉皇，玉皇居殿，如王者之像。侍者七人，冠剑列左右，玉女数百侍卫殿庭。奇异花果，馨香非世所有，玉皇遂问民，具以实对。而民贪顾左右玉女，玉皇曰："汝既悦此侍卫之美乎？"民俯伏请罪，玉皇曰："汝但勤心妙道，自有此等。但汝修行未到，须有功用，不可轻致。"敕左右以玉盘盛仙果示民曰："恣汝以手拱之。"所得之数也，其果绀赤，绝大如拳状，若世之林檎，而芳香无比。自手拱之，所得之数，即侍女之数也。自度尽拱可得十余，遂以手捧之，唯得三枚而已。玉皇曰："此汝分也。"初至未有位

red pearl, an inch in diameter, but just when he was about to grasp it, a boy clothed in red seized it and ran away. The same happened with a green and then a white pearl. Finally, the man, much mortified, placed his hands at the mouth of the bull, and succeeded in securing a black pearl, which he immediately swallowed, to the disgust of a boy dressed in black, who was also awaiting it.

His host now conducted him into the audience hall and presented him to the Emperor of Heaven who, like monarchs on earth, sat on a throne, surrounded by seven ministers of state, splendidly dressed and armed with swords, and several hundred female attendants. Celestial plants and flowers filled the hall with exotic fragrance.

When interrogated, he faithfully recounted to His Majesty how he arrived in Paradise, while his eyes could not help but wander to the beautiful maidens. The emperor noticing it asked if he was not entranced by their beauty, which abashed him very much, so that he begged for forgiveness. The emperor then assured him that if he persisted in his seeking of the Truth, he would one day reach the same state of felicity, but as yet his religious devotions and merits had not reached that stage.

An attendant was commanded to place before the herbalist a large jade salver filled with a kind of celestial fruit, from which he was to grasp as many as two hands could hold. The fruit, of a reddish colour and about the size of a fist, resembled crab apples, but were much more fragrant. The man estimated that he could seize a dozen or so, but as a matter of fact he succeeded in holding only three. "That is your due," the emperor said, adding that since he had just

次,且令前主人领往彼处,敕令三女充侍,别给一屋居之。令诸道侣导以修行,此人遂却至前处,诸道流传授真经,服药用气,洗涤尘念,而三侍女亦授以道术。后数朝谒,每见玉皇,必勉其至意。

其地草木,常如三月中,无荣落寒暑之变。度如人间可一岁余,民自谓仙道已成。忽中夜而叹,左右问,曰:"吾今虽得道,本偶来此耳。来时妻产一女,才经数日,家贫不知复如何,思往一省之。"玉女曰:"君离世已久,妻子等已当亡,岂可复寻?盖为尘念未祛,至此误想。"民

arrived, no place of honour was to be granted him for the time being, and that his host should take him back but allot him a separate room. His Majesty finally ordered that three celestial maidens be sent to wait upon him.

The herbalist returned to his temporary place of lodging, where priests instructed him in devotional exercises, mysterious drugs were administered to him, and hours were spent in solitary meditation and in the training of respiration, while the three maidens assisted him in the pursuit of the Way and the Truth.

Once in a few days he would present himself at the palace audiences, where he received words of encouragement from His Celestial Majesty.

The climate of the place was that of perpetual spring with practically no change of temperature, and the trees and flowers did not experience the rigours of winter. After spending what appeared to him to be more than a year, the man believed that he had found the way to divinity.

However, one night he fell to sighing repeatedly, and, being questioned, said that after all he had arrived in Heaven by accident, and though he was gratified in discovering the Truth, he could not but be reminded of his earthly affairs. When he left his home, his wife had just given birth to a baby girl; being a poor man, he wondered how things were getting on at home. He should like much to pay his wife and daughter a visit. The maidens assured him that he had left the earth for many years, that no doubt his wife and child had long been dead and there was no way of finding them on earth, and that he was thinking of them because he had not entirely divested himself of worldly thoughts. The

曰："今可一岁矣,妻亦当无恙。"要明其事耳,
玉女遂以告诸邻。诸邻共嗟叹之,复白玉皇,
玉皇命遣归。诸仙等于水上作歌乐饮馔以送
之,其三玉女又与之别,各遗以黄金一铤,曰:
"恐至人世,归求无得,以此为费耳。"中女曰:
"君至彼倘无所见,思归。吾有药在金铤中,取
而吞之,可以归矣。"小女谓曰:"恐君为尘念
侵,不复有仙,金中有药,恐不固耳。吾知君家
已无处寻,唯舍东一捣练石尚在,吾已将药置
石下。如金中无,但取此服可矣。"言讫,见一
群鸿鹄,天际飞过。众谓民曰:"汝见此否? 但
从之而去。"众捧民举之,民亦腾身而上,便至
鹄群。鹄亦不相惊扰,与飞空。回顾犹见岸上
人挥手相送,可百来人。

乃至一城中,人物甚众,问其地,乃临海县
也,去蜀已甚远矣。遂鬻其金为资粮,经岁乃

man insisted that he was absent from home only for a year or so and that his family could surely be found; he desired only to confirm personally these facts. The maidens told their neighbours how he felt, and all sighed and deplored his failing.

The matter was ultimately reported to the Emperor of Heaven, who gave permission for the herbalist to return to his earthly home. The various divinities gave a farewell party in his honour on a boat, with music, songs, the best drinks and food, and each of the three maidens presented him with a bar of gold, which they said could be sold, if necessary, to support himself in case he failed to find any relatives at home. One of the maidens said that her bar contained a magic powder, enabling him to return to Heaven on swallowing it. The youngest one suggested that as the powder might lose its affect because of his worldly thoughts, he could find some pills that possessed the same properties under the stone whereon his wife used to do her laundry.

As they were speaking a flock of wild geese came flying by. His friends instructed him to fix his eyes on them, while they raised him on their shoulders and gently pushed him upward. Before he realized what they were doing to him, his body commenced to shoot towards the birds, which did not seem frightened, and they left together, while his friends waved their adieus.

He landed near a large and populous town, which proved to be the county seat of Linhai, many, many miles from Sichuan. It took him a year and much of his gold to reach his home town. It was the last year of Kai Yuan period of the Tang dynasty, and when he enquired about his family, no-

至蜀。时开元末年。问其家，无人知者。有一
人年九十余，云吾祖父往年，因采药不知所之，
至今九十年矣。乃民之孙也，相持而泣，云姑
叔父皆已亡矣，时所生女适人身死，其孙已年
五十余矣。相寻故居，皆为瓦砾荒榛，唯故础
尚在。民乃毁金求药，将吞之，忽失药所在。
遂举石，得一玉合，有金丹在焉。即吞之，而心
中明了，却记去路。此民虽仙洞得道，而本庸
人，都不能详问其事。

　　时罗天师在蜀，见民说其去处，乃云，是第
五洞宝仙九室之天，玉皇即天皇也。大牛乃驮
龙也，所吐珠，赤者吞之，寿与天地齐，青者五
万岁，黄者三万岁，白者一万岁，黑者五千岁。
此民吞黑者，虽不能学道，但于人世上亦得五

body seemed to know.

Finally, he met an old man of ninety years of age, who had a faint recollection that about the time he was born, his grandfather went out to look for herbs and disappeared. The old man was actually the herbalist's grandson, who declared further that his uncles, aunts and his own married daughter had all died, while his own grandchild was about fifty years of age.

Looking for the old home, they found only broken tiles and brambles, but the stone used for laundering the clothes still remained. Having failed to find any divine powder in the gold bar, the herbalist lifted the stone as directed and discovered a small jade casket, wherein was a pill. He swallowed it at once and felt that his mind became much clearer, but he was still unable to recall the way back to Heaven. For though he had obtained some notion of the Truth during his stay in the celestial regions, he was too ignorant fully to appreciate the more profound mysteries.

About that time the Taoist Master Luo was visiting Sichuan and, upon being told of the man's strange experiences, identified the cavern as the Fifth Cave of the Heaven with Nine Sacred Halls, the monarch as the Emperor of Heaven, and the beast as the Dragon of Burden. And lastly, the seven gods standing around the emperor were the seven stars of the Polar Group. As to the pearls, explained the master, anyone swallowing the red pearl would reach an age equal to that of the universe, the green one fifty thousand years, the yellow one thirty thousand, the white one ten thousand, and the black one five thousand years. The herbalist could not become a divinity, continued the high Taoist authority, but

千岁耳。玉帝前立七人，北斗七星也。

民得药服却入山，不知所之，盖去归洞天矣。

he would live to five thousand years of age.

After taking the pill, the herbalist went into the mountains, and nobody knew anything further of his whereabouts. It was suspected that he succeeded after all in finding his way back to the celestial regions.

郗 鉴

牛 肃

荥阳郑曙，著作郎郑虔之弟也。博学多能，好奇任侠。尝因会客，言及人间奇事，曙曰："诸公颇读晋书乎？见太尉郗鉴事迹否？晋书虽言其人死，今则存。"坐客惊曰："愿闻其说。"

曙曰："某所善武威段扬，为定襄令。扬有子曰碧，少好清虚，慕道，不食酒肉。年十六，请于父曰：'愿寻名山，访异人求道。'扬许之，赐钱十万，从其志。

段子天宝五载，行过魏郡，舍于逆旅。逆旅有客焉，自驾一驴，市药数十斤，皆养生辟谷之物也，而其药有难求未备者，日日于市邸谒胡商觅之。碧视此客七十余矣，雪眉霜须，

THE MYSTERY OF
THE MISSING MINISTER
Niu Su

Zheng Shu of Rongyang was renowned for his scholarship and versatility, besides being fond of adventures and addicted to acts of chivalry. At social gatherings he would relate to his friends many a strange tale of his remarkable experiences.

"You have all read the biography of Xi Jian, Minister of State, in the *History of the Jin Dynasty*, and, of course, of his death," he said one day to a company of friends. "But as a matter of fact he did not die, but is still alive."

To satisfy the astonished guests, he told the following story:

His friend Duan Yang, Magistrate of Dingxiang, had a son, whose name was Lüe and who from boyhood was infatuated with the mysteries of Taoism, leading a secluded and meditative life and refraining from the drinking of spirits and the eating of meats. At sixteen years of age he obtained permission from his father to visit the sacred mountains with a view to discovering the Mystic Way from religious and philosophical hermits. The lad was given a hundred thousand copper cash for the expenses of his pilgrimage, and he started on his trip with his father's blessing.

Passing through the prefecture of Wei, he stopped at an inn, where he encountered a traveller accompanied by a mule loaded with herbs. It seemed that the traveller was

而貌如桃花,亦不食谷。碧知是道者,大喜。伺其休暇,市珍果美膳,药食醇醪荐 之。客甚惊,谓碧曰:'吾山叟,市药来此,不愿世人知,子何得觉吾而致此耶?'碧曰:'某虽幼龄,性好虚静。见翁所为,必是道者,故愿欢会。'客悦,为饮至夕,因同宿。数日事毕,将去,谓碧曰:'吾姓孟,名期思,居在恒山,于行唐县西北九十里。子欲知吾名氏如此。'碧又为祖饯,叩头诚祈,愿至山中,谘受道要。叟曰:'若然者,观

meeting with difficulty in obtaining certain rare herbs, for he went daily to the drug shops in search of them.

Lüe noted that the stranger must be more than seventy years of age, yet though his beard and eyebrows were snow-white, his cheeks were pink and ruddy like peach blossoms, and he ate no cereals at all. The lad concluded that his fellow traveller was a man of high religious attainments, and he was delighted with his accidental meeting. He bought some fresh fruit, vegetables of the season, medicinal herbs and balms, and sent them as gifts to the old gentleman.

Greatly surprised, the latter said to Lüe, "I am a hermit from the mountains, having come here to replenish my provisions, and I do not want anyone to know about me. How have you succeeded in learning my status, sending me such nice and appropriate presents?"

Lüe explained his ideals of life and the object of his pilgrimage, and how he had watched the doings of the old gentleman and arrived at his conclusion. "I decided, therefore," he continued, "to meet you in a friendly way and make your acquaintance."

The old hermit felt greatly pleased, and the two spent several days happily together at the inn.

When the hermit had completed his purchases, he got ready to leave the town.

"My name is Meng Qisi," he told Lüe, "and I live on the Heng Mountain, ninety *li* to the north-west of Xingtang County."

The neophyte entertained his hermit friend at a farewell repast, knelt before him and asked for permission to visit the mountain and learn the Way of Truth.

子志坚,可与居矣。然山中居甚苦,须忍饥寒。故学道之人,多生退志。又山中有耆宿,当须启白,子熟计之。'礜又固请,叟知其有志,乃谓之曰:'前至八月二十日,当赴行唐。可于西北行三十里,有一孤姥庄。庄内孤姥,甚是奇人,汝当谒之。因言行意,坐以须我。'礜再拜受约,至期而往。果得此孤庄,老姥出问之,礜具以告姥。姥抚背言曰:'小子年幼若此,而能好道,美哉。'因纳其囊装于柜中,坐礜于堂前阁内。姥家甚富,给礜所须甚厚。居二十日,而孟先生至,顾礜言曰:'本谓率语耳,宁期果来,然吾有事到恒州,汝且居此,数日当返。'如言

"I see that you are determined to find the Way, and I am willing to give you my help," said the old man sympathetically, "but I must warn you of the hardships of mountain life, with its cold and hunger. Many were those who could not live through it and abandoned the search. We have, moreover, an elder, whose permission must be obtained before you can be admitted to our company. You must, therefore, consider carefully all these problems."

Lüe would not be diverted from his ambition, and in the end the old hermit agreed. "You can start for Xingtang on the twentieth day of the eighth moon," he declared. "Proceeding north-eastward thence some thirty *li*, you will arrive at the farm of an old lady, who is a very remarkable woman. Call on her and inform her of your aspiration, and wait there till I come."

The boy followed the instructions. Upon his arrival at the farmhouse, an old lady came out to meet him. She listened intently to his story.

"You are an extraordinary boy," she exclaimed, patting him on the back, "so young and yet so eager to find the Way." She stored his luggage, and arranged a room for him to stay. She appeared to be quite well-off, and showed every hospitality to the young visitor. Some twenty days passed, and Mr. Meng, the hermit, arrived at the old lady's house.

"I really did not take our conversation seriously," he remarked, surprise in his voice, "but you have actually come. Some business takes me to Hengzhou, but I shall return in a few days. Please wait for me."

On his return, however, he told the boy to wait a few

却到，又谓謷曰：'吾更启白耆宿，当与君俱往。'数日复来，令姥尽收掌謷资装，而使謷持随身衣衾往。謷于是从先生入，初行三十里，大艰险，犹能践履。又三十里，即手扪藤葛，足履嵌岩，魂竦汗出而仅能至。其所居也，则东向南向，尽崇山巨石，林木森翠。北面差平，即诸陵岭。西面悬下，层谿千仞。而有良田，山人颇种植其中。有瓦屋六间，前后数架在其北，诸先生居之。东厢有厨灶，飞泉檐间落地，以代汲井。其北户内西二间，为一室，闭其门。东西间为二室，有先生六人居之，其室前庑下，有数架书，三二千卷。谷于石，药物至多，醇酒常有数石。謷既谒诸先生，先生告曰：'夫居山

days longer, as he had to secure the permission of the Elder, after which the two of them would start for their mountain destination.

When the day of departure finally arrived, the old lady was asked to keep the boy's luggage, as the latter should take along with him only the clothes he was wearing and his bed-roll.

The journey to the hermitage was an arduous one: for the first ten miles, while the going was difficult, one could still walk comfortably, but on the second half of the journey one had to climb and crawl, making progress only with the help of vines and protruding branches, as the trail took them over rocks and cliffs. When they arrived at last at the retreat, the boy was bathed in perspiration and overcome by fatigue.

To the south and east the hermitage was encompassed by peaks and huge cliffs, as well as by a thick forest. To the north was a level space, on the edge of which were more wild peaks, while the west side bordered on a precipice of unfathomable depth, with some cultivated land in between. The house where the hermits lived had six rooms with tiled roofs, all facing the south. There was a kitchen on the left and spring water constantly flowed on its roof-top and down a channel, thus saving the hermits from the necessity of a well. Two of the rooms on the west end, which had been transformed into a single large one, remained closed. Two other rooms on the east end were used as sleeping quarters for six of the inmates. The covered veranda was lined with shelves full of books, two or three thousand volumes in all. Barrels of cereals were also stocked there, together with quantities of medicinal herbs and many jars of rice wine.

异于人间，亦大辛苦，须忍饥馁，食药饵。能甘此，乃可居，子能之乎？'裻曰：'能。'于是留止凡五日。孟先生曰：'今日盍谒老先生。'于是启西室，室中有石堂，堂北开直下，临眺川谷。而老先生据绳床，北面而斋心焉。裻敬谒拜老先生，先生良久开目，谓孟叟曰：'是尔所言者耶？此儿佳矣，便与汝充弟子。'于是辞出，又闭户。其庭前临西渊，有松树十株，皆长数仞，其下磐石，可坐百人。则于石中镌局，诸先生休暇，常对棋而饮酒焉。裻为侍者，睹先生棋，皆不工也，因教其形势，诸先生曰：'汝亦晓棋，可坐。'因与诸叟对，叟皆不敌。于是老先生命开户出，植杖临崖而立，西望移时，因顾谓叟可

The boy paid his respects to the hermits, who impressed on him that he could remain with them on the condition that he would be satisfied with the medicinal herbs as food, and not be afraid of gnawing hunger. He nodded his agreement.

Five days later Mr. Meng said to Lüe, "Let me present you to our Elder."

He led the lad into the closed chamber. It was a hall with stone walls, and had a door to the north. From its window one could see verdant valleys and shining streams. The Elder in deep meditation with his eyes closed, was sitting facing the north on a stringed cot. After Lüe had made a deep obeisance before him, he slowly opened his eyes.

"So he's the one you spoke of," said he approvingly to Mr. Meng. "He seems to be quite nice; you may consider him as your pupil." The two asked leave and retired.

Between the building and the precipice on the west was the courtyard, where there were a dozen lofty pines, under which lay flat stones, large and numerous enough to seat a hundred persons. On some of them chessboards had been engraved, and the hermits during their spare hours often played games of chess on them, sipping rice wine the while.

While waiting upon them, Lüe used to watch the games, and noted that his seniors were rather mediocre players. Once he ventured to point out their mistakes; then they invited him to join in the pastime, wherein he found he could easily defeat them.

One day the Elder came out of his room. After standing with the support of a cane on the edge of the precipice, and gazing at the scenery for a little while, he turned and asked if anyone of the hermits would like to play with him. "We

对棋。孟期思曰:'诸人皆不敌此小子。'老先生笑,因坐召翳,与尔对之。既而先生棋少劣于翳,又微笑,谓翳曰:'欲习何艺乎?'翳幼年,不识求方术,而但言愿且受周易。老先生诏孟叟授之,老先生又归室,闭其门。翳习易逾年,而日晓占候布卦,言事若神。翳在山四年,前后见老先生出户,不过五六度。但于室内端坐绳床,正心禅观,动则三百二百日不出。老先生常不多开目,貌有童颜,体至肥充,都不复食。每出禅时,或饮少药汁,亦不识其药名。后老先生忽云:'吾与南岳诸葛仙家为期,今到矣,须去。'翳在山久,忽思家,因请还家省观,即却还。孟先生怒曰:'归即归矣,何却还之有?'因白老先生,先生让孟叟曰:'知此人

are no match for our young friend," declared Mr. Meng.

The Elder sat down and smilingly told the lad to play a game with him, in which Lüe proved to be slightly superior.

The old man smiled and asked Lüe what he sought to learn on the mountain.

Still too young to realize the need for longevity or for learning alchemy, Lüe merely replied, "Please teach me all about the *Classic of Changes*."

The Elder passed the reply on to Mr. Meng, and went back to his room. For more than a year the young man studied with his teacher the oracular arts and fortune-telling, which enabled him later in life to foretell events like a seer.

Lüe spent in all four years on the mountain. During this length of time he saw the Elder outdoors not more than five or six times. For two or three hundred days at a stretch he remained in his own room, mostly sitting on the stringed cot in profound meditation. The Elder rarely opened his eyes. He had the complexion of a boy, and although he ate little, he was quite stout.

Each time he ended his meditation, he would drink a little of a medicinal liquid, the name of which was not generally known. One day Lüe heard him say that he had made an engagement with the Taoist Master Zhuge of the South Mountains, and must go to meet him.

After the young man had spent four years in the mountain retreat, he felt homesick and expressed the desire to be permitted to visit his parents; he promised to return promptly.

Mr. Meng was visibly annoyed. "Go home if you like," he exclaimed, "but don't speak of coming back here."

不终,何与来也?'于是使归。归后一岁,又却
寻诸先生,至则室屋如故,门户封闭,遂无一
人。下山问孤庄老姥,姥曰:'诸先生不来尚一
年矣。'蓉因悔恨殆死。

　　蓉在山间,常问孟叟老先生何姓名,叟取
晋书郗鉴传令读之,谓曰:'欲识老先生,即郗
太尉也。'"

He reported the matter to the Elder, who said, "If you knew that the lad would not stay," the latter complained, "why did you bring him here at all?"

The young man left for his home, and after a year tried to rejoin the hermits. The cottage was there, but the place was locked. He went in search of the old lady. When he found her, she declared that the old gentleman had not visited her place for a whole year. Lüe went home in profound mortification.

When Lüe was living on the mountain, he asked Mr. Meng once about the name of the Elder. His teacher took from the bookshelf the *History of the Jin Dynasty*, and showed him the biography of Xi Jian.

"If you desire to know more of the Elder," said he, "just read this biography." In a word, the Elder was no other than Xi Jian, Minister of State of the Jin dynasty.

上　清　传

　　贞元壬申春三月，相国窦公居光福里第，月夜闲步于中庭。有常所宠青衣上清者，乃曰："今欲启事，郎须到堂前，方敢言之。"窦公亟上堂。上清曰："庭树上有人，恐惊郎，请谨避之。"窦公曰："陆贽久欲倾夺吾权位，今有人在庭树上，吾祸将至。且此事将奏与不奏皆受祸，必窜死于道路。汝在辈流中不可多得，吾身死家破，汝定为宫婢。圣君若顾问，善为我辞焉。"上清泣曰"诚如是，死生以之！"

THE FAITHFUL HANDMAID
Anonymous

In the third moon of the year Ren Shen during the Zhen Yuan period of the Tang dynasty, Prime Minister Dou Cen, whose mansion was situated in the Lane of Blessed Light, was strolling leisurely in the middle of his courtyard on a moonlit night.

A favourite handmaid by the name of Shang Qing came and whispered to him, "May I suggest that Your Excellency proceed at once inside the house, as I have something to report which I dare not say out here."

They hurriedly entered the building.

"My Lord," she blurted out, "a man is hiding in one of the trees in the courtyard; I was afraid that he might frighten you. That is why I requested you to come inside."

"Lu Zhi has long plotted to undermine my position and replace me in my high post," muttered the prime minister. "I am convinced that the man in the tree forebodes the arrival of disaster. Whether I report the incident to the throne or not, disgrace will overtake me, and I shall surely die by the roadside while on my way to exile. You are an exceptional girl, and when I am dead and my family ruined, you will certainly become a serving maid at court. In case His Majesty should talk to you about me, please speak well of me."

"If unfortunately your words should become true," replied Shang Qing in tears, "I will carry out your instructions even

窦公下阶,大呼曰:"树上君子,应是陆贽使来。能全老夫性命,敢不厚报!"树上人应声而下,乃衣缞粗者也。曰:"家有大丧,贫甚,不办葬礼。伏知相公推心济物,所以卜夜而来,幸相公无怪。"公曰:"某罄所有,堂封绢千匹而已。方拟修私庙,次今且辍赠,可乎?"缞者拜谢,窦公答之如礼。又曰:"便辞相公,请左右赍所赐绢掷于墙外,某先于街中俟之。"窦公依其请。命仆,使侦其绝踪且久,方敢归寝。

翌日,执金吾先奏其事,窦公得次,又奏之。德宗厉声曰:"卿交通节将,蓄养侠刺,位

at the risk of death."

The prime minister then descended from the terrace to the courtyard.

"You man in the tree," he shouted, "you must be an assassin sent by Lu Zhi. I'll reward you heavily if you'll only spare my old life." The man descended from the tree; he was dressed in rough sackcloth.

"My parent is dead," he confessed, "and I am too poor to pay for the burial. I know Your Excellency is generous and charitably inclined, so I've ventured to make this nocturnal visit. I humbly hope that I have not upset you."

"I'll give you all the silk that I have in store, namely, a thousand rolls," replied the prime minister. "I intended to use their worth in restoring my family shrine, but you can have them now as a present from me."

The man in heavy mourning knelt on the ground to express his thanks, which the minister suitably acknowledged.

"In taking my departure," requested the visitor, "may I ask that the silk be thrown over the wall, while I wait outside?"

The request was acceded to, and the servants were ordered to watch closely till the man had disappeared. Then and only then did Dou Cen dare to retire to his bedchamber.

The following morning it was the police who first reported the incident to the throne, and when the premier's turn came, he gave his version.

"You," shouted His Majesty in a loud and angry voice, "you dare to cultivate treasonable relations with my garrison officers and to shelter and patronize swordsmen and assassins in your residence. Your official position close to the throne

崇台鼎，更欲何求！"窦公顿首曰："臣起自刀笔
小才，官已至贵，皆陛下奖拔，实不由人。今不
幸至此，抑乃仇家所为耳。陛下忽震雷霆之
怒，臣便合万死。"中使下殿宣曰："卿且归私
第，待候进止。"越月，贬郴州别驾。会宣武节
度使刘士宁通好于郴州，廉使条疏上闻。德宗
曰："交通节将，信而有征。"流窦于骦州，没入
家资。一簪不着身，竟未达流所，诏自尽。

　　上清果隶名掖庭。后数年，以善应对，能

is already the highest in the land, what other ambition and objective do you harbour in your heart?"

"Your liege servant," submitted the premier, as he prostrated himself before the throne, "commenced his career as a humble scholar. It has been due entirely to Your Majesty's grace and favour, and not at all to his personal qualifications, that he has arrived at the highest rung of the official ladder. The present misunderstanding is the result of the machinations of my political enemies, but in view of Your Majesty's anger, which is comparable to a thunderbolt, your liege deserves a thousand deaths."

A court official then proclaimed the imperial pleasure that the premier should retire to and remain confined in his residence, and there await the final decision. After the lapse of a month Dou Cen was degraded to be the Magistrate of Chenzhou.

Subsequently Liu Shining, the Garrison Commander at Xuanwu, sent a mission of amity to Chenzhou, about which the provincial authorities made a report to the emperor.

"Now," declared His Majesty, "we have concrete evidence of his cultivating traitorous relationships with our garrison officers."

The ex-premier was ordered to be banished to Huanzhou, and his private property was confiscated, not excepting even a single hairpin. Before he reached his place of exile, an imperial edict gave him permission to commit suicide.

Shang Qing, as foretold by her master, became a maid in the imperial court, and after serving for a few years, in which she showed great versatility in conversation and exceptional skill in preparing tea, she was more than once called

煎茶，数得在帝左右。德宗曰："宫掖间人数不少，汝了事，从何得至此？"上清对曰："妾本故宰相窦参家女奴。窦某妻早亡，故妾得陪扫洒。及窦某家破，幸得填宫。既侍龙颜，如在天上。"德宗曰："窦某罪不止养侠刺，亦甚有赃污，前时纳官银器至多。"上清流涕而言曰："窦某自御史中丞，历度支、户部、盐铁三使，至宰相，首尾六年，月入数十万。前后非时赏赐。当也不知纪极，乃者郴州所送纳官银物，皆是恩赐。当部录日，妾在郴州，亲见州县希陆贽意旨刮去。所进银器，上刻作藩镇官衔姓名，

to wait upon the emperor himself.

"The palace has innumerable attendants," once the emperor said to her, "and you are not so young. How has it happened that you are here?"

"Your Majesty's slave," she replied, "was a bondmaid in the home of the late Prime Minister Dou. Her Ladyship died early, so your slave assisted in the management of his household. When his home was disrupted, I entered the service of the imperial palace. Honoured to have the opportunity to feast my eyes on the imperial countenance, I feel as if I were living in Heaven."

"Dou's crimes did not end with his keeping of swordsmen and assassins, he was also very corrupt," declared the emperor in a reminiscent mood. "When his private property was confiscated, there was found an enormous quantity of silverwares."

"Dou Cen," explained Shang Qing with tears, "was promoted from the post of Censor to be Minister of Finance, taking complete charge of the empire's revenue, until he was appointed prime minister. In all he served for six years, and his monthly emoluments were several hundred thousand taels. Besides, from time to time Your Majesty showered presents on him. The silver vessels that were discovered in his home when the property was confiscated, were all bestowed on him by Your Majesty. When I was at Chenzhou at the time of expropriation, the local magistrate, in order to curry favour with the Minister of State, Lu Zhi, gave orders that the engraved characters on the silver vessels be erased and replaced with the names of garrison commanders, so as to cast suspicion on Dou Cen for bribery and high treason. I

诬为赃物。伏乞下验之。"于是宣索窦某没官银器覆视，其刮字处，皆如上清言。时贞元十二年。德宗又问蓄养侠刺事，上清曰："本实无，悉是陆贽陷害，使人为之。"德宗怒陆贽，曰："这獠奴我脱却伊绿衫，便与紫衫着，又常唤伊作陆九。我任窦参，方称意，次须教我枉杀却他。及至权入伊手，甚为软弱，甚于泥团。"乃下诏雪窦参。时裴延龄探知陆贽恩衰，得恣行媒孽。贽竟受谴不回。

后上清特敕丹书度为女道士，终嫁为金忠

saw this with my own eyes. Your Majesty can make enquiries and ascertain if my statement is true."

The silver vessels were sent for, and on examining the bottoms, the emperor found that what Shang Qing had affirmed was correct. This happened in the twelfth year of Zhen Yuan.

Then His Majesty enquired about the former prime minister's employing swordsmen and assassins. Shang Qing replied that Dou did no such thing, and that the report was fabricated by Lu Zhi, who wanted to incriminate his enemy. His Majesty awoke as from a nightmare.

"Ah, the wicked knave!" cried His Majesty angrily. "I had his green gown replaced by a robe of purple, and have often called him by his pet name of Lu the Ninth, but when Dou Cen was serving me to my hearty contentment, it was he who incited me to kill him. When he later took over the premiership, he did not know how to use his power, and he was as soft as a ball of mud."

An imperial edict was soon promulgated establishing the innocence of the late Prime Minister Dou Cen. When Pei Yanling, Lu's rival at court, learned that the latter had fallen into disgrace, he plotted day and night to destroy Lu, who in consequence received severe punishment and never returned to office.

Shang Qing, the faithful handmaid, obtained permission from the emperor to enter a nunnery, but in the end married a man by the name of Jin Zhongyi. Although Lu Zhi fell

义妻。世以陆贽门生名位多显达者，世不可传说，故此事绝无人知。

from his high estate, he had numerous influential followers at court, so that until now his wicked actions to ruin Dou Cen have been prevented from being made known to the world at large.

李师师外传

阙　名

李师师者,汴京东二厢永庆坊,染局匠王寅之女也。寅妻既产女而卒,寅以菽浆代乳乳之。得不死,在襁褓未尝啼。

汴俗凡男女生,父母爱之,必为舍身佛寺。寅怜其女,乃为舍身宝光寺。女时方知孩笑,一老僧目之曰:"此何地,尔乃来耶?"女至是忽啼,僧为摩其顶,啼乃止。寅窃喜曰:"是女真佛弟子。"为佛弟子者,俗呼为师,故名之曰师师。

师师方四岁,寅犯罪系狱死。师师无所归,有倡籍李姥者,收养之。比长,色艺绝伦,遂名冠诸坊曲。

LOVE AND LOYALTY
OF A COURTESAN
Anonymous

Li Shishi was the daughter of a dyer by the name of Wang Yin, who lived in the eastern suburbs of Kaifeng, then the capital of the Song Empire. Her mother died soon after giving birth to her, and it was her father who raised her on millet gruel for want of milk. She rarely cried as a baby.

According to the local custom, children deeply beloved by their parents must be nominally adopted by some Buddhist temple in order to be saved from dying early, and as Wang Yin was very fond of his baby girl, he had her adopted by the Temple of the Sacred Nimbus.

"Don't you know what sort of a place this is, and yet you dare to come here?" said the old monk, gazing at the infant.

At these words the child commenced to cry. Then the priest rubbed the crown of her head with the palm of his hand and she stopped crying. Her father was delighted, saying that she was certainly destined to be a Buddhist disciple. Now the disciples of Buddhism were familiarly called *shi* (teacher), so she was given the name Shishi.

When she was four years old, her father was sentenced for some criminal offence, and died in the prison. The child was left without a home, and Old Lady Li, a keeper of a house of pleasure, adopted her. As she grew in age, she excelled both in physical beauty and in her vocal art, and became the most famous of all the courtesans in the capital.

　　徽宗皇帝即位，好事奢华，而蔡京章惇王黼之徒，遂假绍述为名，劝帝复行青苗诸法。长安中粉饰为饶乐气象，市肆酒税，日计万缗，金玉缯帛，充溢府库。于是童贯朱勔辈，复导以声色狗马，宫室苑囿之乐，凡海内奇花异石，搜采殆遍。筑离宫于汴城之北，名曰艮岳。帝般乐其中，久而厌之，更思微行为狎邪游。内押班张迪者，帝所新幸之寺人也。未宫时，为长安狎客，往来诸坊曲，故与李姥善。为帝言陇西氏色艺双绝，帝艳心焉。翼日，命迪出内府紫茸二匹，霞氍二端，瑟瑟珠二颗，白金廿

Now the Emperor Hui Zong of the Song Dynasty, who had just assumed the imperial yellow, initiated a reign of luxury and extravagance. The Prime Minister Cai Jing and his gang had succeeded, in the name of restoring some of the financial reforms of the preceding reigns, in introducing various onerous taxes to raise funds for court expenditures. The capital took on a false and superficial air of wealth and prosperity. The duty on spirits alone amounted daily to ten thousand strings of cash, and the imperial treasury overflowed with gold, silver, jade and silks. The courtiers and favourites pandered to the young sovereign with the pleasures of wine, women and song, of hunting dogs and racing ponies, and with the lavish construction of palaces and gardens. Exotic and rare plants, bizarre and costly rocks, were transported from all over the empire to beautify the imperial pleasure grounds. To the north of the city a luxurious mansion was built, where His Majesty and his boon companions spent days and nights in wild dissipation.

However, the emperor was soon surfeited with these orgies and diversions, and desired to visit incognito the houses of joy in the capital. A eunuch, Zhang, an imperial favourite, used to be a gay young blade before he mutilated himself and entered the service of the palace. He knew Old Lady Li very well, as he had frequented many such houses in former days, hers among them, and he boasted to the emperor of the extraordinary beauty and talent of Li Shishi.

The emperor fell to the temptation, and the following day ordered Zhang to convey to Old Lady Li valuable gifts of silks, velvet, pearls and silver shoes, all from the imperial treasury, and to inform her that a wealthy merchant by the

镒,诡云大贾赵乙,愿过庐一顾。姥利金币,喜诺。

暮夜,帝易服杂内寺四十余人中,出东华门二里许,至镇安坊。镇安坊者,李姥所居之里也。帝麾止余人,独与迪翔步而入。堂户卑庳,姥出迎,分庭抗礼,慰问周至。进以时果数种,中有香雪藕,水晶苹婆,而鲜枣大如卵,皆大官所未供者。帝为各尝一枚,姥复款洽良久,独未见师师出拜。帝延伫以待,时迪已辞退,姥乃引帝至一小轩,棐几临窗,缥缃数帙,窗外新篁,参差弄影。帝翛然兀坐,意兴闲适,

name of Zhao Yi would like to visit her house. Impressed with the presents, she gladly assented to the proposal. At night His Majesty changed his clothes and, mingling among some two score of eunuchs who accompanied him, left the palace by the Dong Hua Gate, arriving soon at Li's establishment. At the door he waved his hand at the others to return, while he and Zhang boldly entered.

The house was a small and modest one, but the mistress was exceptionally warm in the reception of her guests. She set forth before them freshly cut pieces of lotus root, dates (chinese "dates" are not the palm dates of world commerce, but a fruit. In the dried from they are like the dates in colour and delicious in flavour.) as large as eggs, and many other kinds of fruit rarely seen even in the palace. The emperor helped himself to one of each kind, while the old lady continued to entertain him with gossip and small talk. But Shishi was nowhere to be seen though His Majesty patiently waited.

After a while the eunuch retired, and Li conducted her guest to a small kiosk, charmingly furnished and with windows elegantly curtained, through which he could see young bamboo plants in the moonlight gently wafted by the breeze and casting their shadows here and there. The emperor was much delighted with the cozy boudoir and waited contentedly, though Shishi still failed to show herself.

Then, Old Lady Li took the distinguished visitor to a room in the rear, where were laid out on a dining table many dishes of venison, chicken, fish and lamb, all deliciously prepared, with rice of special fragrance, whereof he partook a bowl, she continuing to entertain him. Again, His Majesty was disappointed in that the famous beauty did not appear in

独未见师师出侍。少顷，姥引帝到后堂，陈列
鹿炙鸡酢，鱼脍羊臛等肴，饭以香子稻米，帝为
进一餐，姥侍旁款语移时，而师师终未出见。
帝方疑异，而姥忽复请浴，帝辞之，姥至帝前耳
语曰："儿性好洁，勿忤。"帝不得已，随姥至一
小楼下湢室中，浴竟，姥复引帝坐后堂。肴核
水陆，杯盏新洁，劝帝欢饮，而师师终未一见。
良久，姥才执烛引帝至房，帝搴帷而入，一灯荧
然，亦绝无师师在。帝益异之，为倚徙几榻间，
又良久，见姥拥一姬，姗姗而来。淡妆不施脂
粉，衣绢素，无艳服，新浴方罢，娇艳如出水芙
蓉。见帝意似不屑，貌殊倨，不为礼，姥与帝耳
语曰："儿性颇愎，勿怪。"帝于灯下凝睇物色
之，幽姿逸韵，闪烁惊眸。问其年不答，复强
之，乃迁坐他所。姥复附帝耳曰："儿性好静
坐，唐突，勿罪。"遂为下帷而出，师师乃起解玄

his presence.

At this moment of bewilderment he was invited by the old lady to take a bath, which he refused.

"Don't be offended," she whispered to him, "but my dear daughter has a passion for cleanliness!"

His Majesty could not help but follow the old woman into a small bathroom, and after making his ablutions, was led back to the dining room where the table had been set anew with dainties and refreshments. He was urged to drink to his fill, but — all by himself!

After another long wait, Old Lady Li, holding a lighted candle, introduced him to a bedchamber, where he saw a lonely lamp standing behind the door curtain. He was more than amazed, but concealed his annoyance by reposing himself now in a chair, now on the couch. After long last Li returned to the room, leading by the hand a young woman, who walked slowly and hesitatingly. She wore her natural complexion, using neither powder nor rouge, and seemed to have emerged fresh from a bath. She was as pretty as a lily on the surface of the water, but she manifested little interest in her visitor. In fact, she held herself in rather a cold and haughty posture and hardly acknowledged his presence.

"Please don't take offence," Li whispered in the guest's ear. "My child is obstinate by nature."

His Majesty stared at her intently in the lamplight, and was deeply impressed by her beautiful face and the brilliancy of her eyes, which shone with an air of surprise. He asked to know her age, but she made no reply, and when he insisted, she merely shifted to another seat. Li again told the visitor under her breath that the girl did not like to talk much,

绢褐祆，衣轻绨，卷右袂，援壁间琴，隐几端座，
而鼓平沙落雁之曲。轻拢慢撚，流韵淡远，帝
不觉为之倾耳。遂忘倦，比曲三终，鸡唱矣。
帝亟披帷出，姥闻亦起，为进杏酥饮，枣糕馎饦
诸点品。帝饮杏酥杯许，旋起去。内侍从行
者，皆潜候于外，即拥卫还宫，时大观三年八月
十七日事也。姥私语师师曰："赵人礼意不薄，
汝何落落乃尔？"师师怒曰："彼贾奴耳，我何为
者！"姥笑曰："儿强项，可令御史里行。"已而长
安人言藉藉，皆知驾幸陇西氏。姥闻大恐，日
夕惟涕泣，泣语师师曰："洵是，夷吾族矣。"师
师曰："无恐，上肯顾我，岂忍杀我？且畴昔之

and that he should not mind her seeming rudeness. She then retired.

Shishi left her chair to remove her outer coat of yellow satin and, rolling up the sleeves of her soft clinging gown, reached for her lute hanging on the wall. Placing the instrument on a long table and sitting down by its side, she played the classical tune of the *Wild Geese's Descent on the Smooth Sands*, and the melody as well as the lightness of touch of her fingers fascinated the imperial ears, making him forget his drowsiness.

By the time she finished the third and last part of the piece, the cocks had begun to crow. The emperor hurriedly raised the door curtain to leave, and the old lady reappeared, bringing cakes and almond sauce. He took his departure shortly after, his escort waiting discreetly at the door, and returned to the palace. This happened on the seventeenth day of the eighth moon in the third year of the Da Guan period.

When alone by themselves Li complained cautiously to Shishi. "That Mr. Zhao," she said, "treated you not badly; why were you so cool and indifferent?"

"Why," she answered angrily, "he is nothing but a contemptible shopkeeper. What did he expect of me?"

"You are stiff-necked enough to qualify you to be a censor," retorted the old woman with a laugh.

Before long, gossip began to circulate in the capital about the imperial nocturnal visit to the house of joy, and when Li heard of it, she was terrified. She wept day and night, saying to Shishi that if the report was true, it meant the death of her entire family.

"Never fear," said Shishi, "if His Majesty deigned to call

夜，幸不见逼，上意必怜我。惟是我所窃自悼者，实命不犹，流落下贱，使不洁之名，上累至尊，此则死有余辜耳。若夫天威震怒，横被诛戮，事起佚游，上所深讳，必不至此，可无虑也。"次年正月，帝遣迪赐师师蛇跗琴。蛇跗琴者，琴古而漆黔黬则有纹如蛇之跗，盖大内珍藏宝器也，又赐白金五十两。三月，帝复微行如陇西氏，师师仍淡妆素服，俯伏门阶迎驾。帝喜，为执其手令起。帝见其堂户忽华敞，前所御处，皆以蟠龙锦绣覆其上。又小轩改造杰阁，画栋朱阑，都无幽趣。而李姥见帝至，亦避匿。宣至，则体颤不能起，无复向时调寒送暖情态。帝意不悦，为霁颜以老娘呼之。谕以一

on me, he would surely not kill me. Moreover, he put no compulsion of any kind on me that night, proving that he had pity and love for me. What saddens me is that my fate in life is ill-starred — lowering me to such a social level as to bring infamy by association to the noble sovereign. For my being guilty of this, even death itself cannot atone. There is no need of fear of punishment for having offended His Majesty, because, the whole affair being one of gallantry, the emperor would surely try to keep it quiet."

When the New Year came, His Majesty bestowed on Shishi the ancient and renowned instrument known as the Lute of the Snake's Skin (a treasure of the palace, so-called because the woodwork was varnished in the pattern and colour of a serpent's skin) and, in addition, fifty taels of pure silver.

In the third moon of the following year His Majesty paid his second incognito visit to Shishi. When the latter, still plainly dressed, met the imperial guest on her knees, he smilingly raised her to her feet. He noticed that the house had been entirely renovated and extended, and the rooms he previously visited had their furniture covered with satin embroidered with the imperial dragon. The quiet kiosk had been transformed into a big pavilion with vermilion columns and bright red railings, losing completely its former air of elegance.

Old Lady Li hid herself somewhere inside, and when summoned to the imperial presence, trembled all over, all her previous familiarity and loquacity having vanished. His Majesty, inwardly displeased, put on an appearance of amiability, addressing her as Old Mother, and informing her that

家子,无拘畏。姥拜谢,乃引帝至大楼,楼初
成,师师伏地叩帝赐额。时楼前杏花盛放,帝
为书醉杏楼三字赐之。少顷置酒,师师侍侧,
姥匍匐传樽为帝寿。帝赐师师隅坐,命鼓所赐
蛇跗琴,为弄梅花三叠。帝衔杯饮听,称善者
再。帝见所供肴馔器皿,皆龙凤形,或镂或绘,
悉如宫中式。因问之,知出自尚食房厨夫手,
姥出金钱倩制者。帝亦不怿,谕姥今后悉如
前,无矜张显著,遂不终席,驾返。

　　帝尝御书院,出诗句试诸画工,中式者岁
间得一二。是年九月,以"金勒马嘶芳草地,玉

all the three of them being now of one family, she should not feel constrained or nervous. She prostrated herself on the floor to express her gratefulness.

His Majesty was then conducted to a newly built hall and Shishi, falling on her knees, begged the emperor to dedicate it. His eyes were met by the apricot trees in full bloom in front of the building, so he wrote three big characters meaning "The Hall of Intoxicating Apricot Blossoms."

Soon the table was set; Shishi waited on His Majesty, while on bent knees Old Lady Li offered wine in honour of the emperor's longevity. Shishi was granted a seat on one side and commanded to play on the royal gift of the famous lute, the tune she chose being the classical *Playing Thrice for the Plum Blossoms*. Drinking and listening, His Majesty applauded heartily when the melody ended.

The emperor noted that the table-wares were painted with dragons and phoenixes, like those employed in the palace, and enquired where they originated. He was informed by Li that they were specially ordered at her own expense after the model provided by the cooks of the imperial household. Annoyed by the information, he warned her to continue in her former plain style of living and not indulge in ostentation. The dinner broke up somewhat abruptly on account of the incident.

His Majesty used to honour the Imperial Academy of Fine Arts with personal visits, when he would test the artists by commanding them to paint pictures with lines of poetry as themes. One or two pictures would be crowned each year with imperial awards. That year in the ninth moon a picture was painted having for its subject the following two lines:

楼人醉杏化天。"名画一幅,赐陇西氏。又赐藕
丝灯,煖雪灯,芳苡灯,火凤衔珠灯,各十盏。鸬
鹚杯,琥珀杯,琉璃盏,镂金偏提,各十事。月团
凤团蒙顶等茶百斤,馎饦寒具银馅饼数盒。又
赐黄白金各千两。时宫中已盛传其事,郑后闻
而谏曰:"妓流下贱,不宜不接圣躬。且暮夜微
行,亦恐事生叵测,愿陛下自爱。"帝颔之,阅岁
者再,不复出。然通问赏赐,未尝绝也。宣和二
年,帝复幸陇西氏,见悬所赐画于醉杏楼,观玩
久之。忽回顾见师师,戏语曰:"画中人,乃呼之
竟出耶。"即日赐师师辟寒金钿,映月珠环,
舞鸾青镜,金虬香鼎,次日又赐师师端溪凤味

Chewing bits of gold the ponies neigh softly
on the grass-green sward,
While in the House of Jade, the Lady drinks
to the apricot flowers.

This painting was bestowed on Shishi. In addition she was given highly precious and artistic lanterns, ten of each kind, having such fanciful names as Silken Fibres of the Lotus Root, Warming Up in the Snow, Fragrant Tulip, and the Fiery Phoenix Holding a Pearl in the Mouth; four sets of bejewelled wine-cups, ten in each set; a hundred pounds each of three kinds of exquisite tea; different makes of delicious cakes; and one thousand taels each of gold and silver.

The affair soon became the topic of gossip in court circles. Her Majesty the Empress Zheng, getting knowledge of it, remonstrated with the emperor, appealing to his good sense which, she pleaded, should not allow him to associate with a courtesan. Besides, she pointed out, going out of the palace incognito at night might lead to some untoward incident. His Majesty nodded in approval of her words. For almost two years he refrained from leaving clandestinely the palace precincts, but there continued a stream of messages and gifts for Shishi.

In the second year of the Xuan He period His Majesty again honoured Shishi with a visit, and saw the painting which he had bestowed on her hung up in the Hall of Intoxicating Apricot Blossoms. Gazing at it for a long while, he suddenly turned and caught sight of Shishi. "Hello," he laughingly cried, "the beauty in the picture responds to my call."

He had brought from the palace wonderful hairpins of

砚,李廷珪墨,玉管宣毫笔,剡溪绫纹纸,又赐李姥钱百千缗。迪私言于上曰:"帝幸陇西,必易服夜行,故不能常继。今艮岳离宫东偏,有官地衮延二三里,直接镇安坊。若于此处为潜道,帝驾往还殊便。"帝曰:"汝图之。"于是迪等疏言离宫宿卫人,向多露处,臣等愿捐赀若干,于官地营室数百楹,广筑围墙,以便宿卫。帝可其奏。于是羽林巡军等,布列至镇安坊止,而行人为之屏迹矣。四年三月,帝始从潜道幸陇西。赐藏阄双陆等具,又赐片玉棋盘,碧白二色玉棋子,画院宫扇,九折五花之簟,鳞文蓐

gold, strings of pearls, a handmirror ornamented with a dancing phoenix and an incense-burner encircled by a golden dragon. To these gifts were added the next day a stone ink-slab carved with the phoenix, blocks of ink manufactured by the famous inkmaker Li Tinggui, writing brushes of fine hair and jade holders, and paper made of silk. Old Lady Li received as present a large sum of silver.

The eunuch Zhang now slyly suggested to His Majesty that visiting surreptitiously at night the home of Shishi was after all inconvenient and could not be often repeated. Now, he said, the imperial chateau outside of the capital and her house were separated only by a piece of vacant public land, a few hundred yards in length. If a private enclosed passage were built between the two places, the problem would be solved. His Majesty commanded the eunuch to execute the scheme.

Using as pretext that the palace guards were obliged to live in the open, Zhang and a few others in a formal petition recommended the building of barracks for the soldiers on the vacant public land, to be surrounded with a high wall. When the building was completed a safe and secret access was provided for His Majesty so Shishi's quarters, and on account of the presence of the guards the populace kept away from the neighbourhood.

In the third moon of the fourth year the emperor commenced his visits to Shishi by the newly provided route. He again showered presents on her, including dominoes and dice of ivory, a chessboard of jade and chess pieces of precious green and white stones, elegant fans painted by the artists of the Imperial Academy of Fine Arts, expensive mats and cur-

叶之席，湘竹绮帘，五采珊瑚钩。是日帝与师
师双陆不胜，围棋又不胜，赐白金二千两。嗣
后师师生辰，又赐珠钿金条脱各二事，玑琲一
篚，氀锦数端，鹭毛缯翠羽缎百匹，白金千两。
后又以灭辽庆贺，大赉州郡，加恩官府。乃赐
师师紫绡绢幕，五采流苏，冰蚕神锦被，却尘锦
褥，麸金千两，良酝则有桂露流霞香蜜等名，又
赐李姥大府钱万缗。计前后赐金银钱缯帛器
用食物等，不下十万。帝尝于宫中，集宫眷等
宴坐，韦妃私问曰："何物李家儿，陛下悦之如
此？"帝曰："无他，但令尔等百人，改艳妆，服玄
素，令此娃杂处其中，迥然自别。其一种幽资
逸韵，要在色容之外耳，无何。"

　　帝禅位，自号为道君教主，退处太乙宫。
佚游之兴，于是衰矣。师师语姥曰："吾母子嘻

tains of fine bamboo with hooks of jade. Losing good-hu-
mouredly to her in both games of dice and chess, he presented to her two thousand taels of pure silver. On her birthday
she received two filigrees richly bedecked with pearls, and
two gold bracelets, a box of precious stones, bolts of brocades, silks and another thousand taels of silver. On a sub-
sequent occasion celebrating the military victory over the
Northern barbarian, when honours and promotions were generally conferred on civil and army officials, Shishi received
her bountiful share of gifts, including curtains of purple
gauze with brightly coloured tassels, bed covers of brocade,
a thousand taels of gold and jars of famous wines. In all she
and Old Lady Li received gifts of objects and money
amounting in value to one hundred thousand taels of silver.

Once His Majesty and the court ladies were assembled at a
banquet. "What is this Li woman who seems to have bewitched Your Majesty?" he was quietly asked by the imperial
consort Wei.

"Oh, nothing," he replied, "but if the hundred of you ladies discarded your gorgeous costumes and replaced them
with simple dresses, with Shishi standing in your midst, you
will find her absolutely different. She has an air of quiet elegance and a carriage of sylphs and fairies entirely aside from
her wonderful complexion and features."

Some years later His majesty abdicated, adopting the title
of Pope of the Taoist Church and residing in an independent
palace. He lost interest in the vain and idle pleasures of the
flesh.

"You and I," observed Shishi one day to her mother,
"live so happily that we have no idea when a sudden disaster

嘻,不知祸之将及。"姥曰:"然则奈何?"师师曰:"汝第勿与知,唯我所欲。"是时金人方启衅,河北告急。师师乃集前后所赐金钱,呈牒开封尹,愿入官助河北饷。复赂迪等代请于上皇,愿弃家为女冠,上皇许之,赐北郭慈云观居之。未几,金人破汴,主帅闼懒索师师云,金主知其名,必欲生得。乃索累日不得,张邦昌等为踪迹之,以献金营。师师骂曰:"吾以贱妓,蒙皇帝眷,宁一死,无他志。若辈高爵厚禄,朝廷何负于汝,乃事事为斩灭宗社计。今又北面事丑虏,冀得一当为呈身之地,吾岂作若辈羔

will bring us to ruin."

Li asked her what should they do then.

"You had better live in a place which nobody would know, and let me do the rest according to my own judgement," Shishi replied.

At the time the Jin nomadic tribes had already started hostilities against the empire, and north China appealed for military aid. Shishi gathered together all the gold and silver bestowed on her by the emperor and sent it, accompanied by a letter addressed to the Prefect of Kaifeng, as a contribution to the war-chest. At the same time, through bribing the eunuch Zhang, she got word to His Majesty for permission to become a nun, and the latter bestowed on her the Temple of the Merciful Cloud outside the North Gate.

Before long the Jin invaders captured the capital. Their commanding general went in search of Shishi, for the King of the Jins had heard of her name and insisted on having her captured alive. For many days she could not be discovered, then the traitor officials Zhang Bangchang and others trailed her to the temple, and offered her to the Jin commander.

"I am but a humble woman of the house of joy," Shishi railed at them bitterly. "But since I have been honoured by the love of His Majesty, I have no ambition now other than to die. You people have occupied high official positions and received handsome emoluments; in what way has the throne treated you unkindly that you do your best to destroy the dynasty? You now serve as slaves to the wretched savages, hoping to find in me a suitable present with which to ingratiate yourselves with them. I will never let myself be the vicarious lamb or the sacrificial wild goose for you black-

雁赘耶?"乃脱金簪自刺其喉,不死,折而吞之,乃死。道君帝在五国城,知师师死状,犹不自禁其泣涕之决澜也。

guards."

She took her gold hairpin and pierced her throat with it, but failed to kill herself; then she bent and swallowed it, finding her death that way.

Later when the former emperor in exile heard of her tragic death, he wept inconsolably.

梁太祖优待文士

张齐贤

　　梁主之初兼四镇也,英威刚狠,视之若乳
虎,左右小忤其旨,立杀之。梁之职吏,每日先
与家人辞诀而入,归必相贺。宾客对之,不寒
而栗。进士杜荀鹤,以所业投之,且乞一见。
掌客以事闻于梁祖,梁祖默无所报。荀鹤住大
梁数月,先是凡有求谒梁祖,如已通姓名,而未
得见者,虽窬年困踬于逆旅中,寒饿殊甚,主者
留之,不令私去。不尔,即公人辈及祸矣。

　　荀鹤逐日诣客次,一旦,梁祖在便听,谓左

TYRANT AND SCHOLARS
Zhang Qixian

The founder of the dynasty of Liang was notorious for his ferocity, cruelty and tyranny. After he had unified the four principal military districts under his single command, he was feared as if he was the king of beasts. Anyone in his service who incurred his displeasure in the slightest degree would be immediately beheaded. When the officials of Liang left their homes in the morning to go to court, they would bid eternal farewell to their kin, and when they returned safe and sound in the evening, the whole family would rejoice — so uncertain were they of their lives. His guests, when they were received in audience, trembled as if from bitter wintry cold.

A doctor of literature by the name of Du Xunhe sought service under the Lord of Liang, requesting an interview. His card was presented by an attendant, but His Lordship gave no indication whatever of his pleasure. As a result, Du was kept waiting for several months in his inn. For the rule was that the innkeeper must not permit any guest to depart, once his name had been registered at the palace for an audience, though he might have stayed for as long as a year, suffering from cold and hunger in his lodgings. Otherwise, the hotel-keeper was liable to meet with serious trouble in case the guest should at last be summoned to court and not be present.

Du went daily to the palace waiting-room for news of the

右曰："杜荀鹤何在?"左右以见在客次为对。未见间,有驰骑至者。梁祖见之,至巳午间,方退。染祖遽起归宅,荀鹤谓掌客者曰:"某饥甚,欲告归。"公人辈为设食,且曰乞命,若大王出要见秀才,言已归馆舍,即某等求死不暇。至未申间,梁祖果出,复坐于便听,令取骰子来。既至,梁祖掷,意似有所卜。掷且久,终不惬旨,怒甚。屡顾左右,左右怖惧,缩颈重足,若蹈汤火。须臾,梁祖取骰子在手,大呼曰:"杜荀鹤。"掷之六只俱赤,乃连声命屈秀才,荀鹤为主客者引入,令趋,骤至阶陛下,梁祖言曰:"秀才不合趋阶。"荀鹤声喏,恐惧流汗,再

audience. One morning His Lordship was sitting in his reception room and enquired of his retainers where Du was, and they replied that he was present in the waiting-room. Before he could be summoned, however, some important personage arrived on horseback at the palace, and was immediately received by His Lordship. When the guest departed, it was already after noon and His Lordship retired to his private apartments.

Du became very hungry, so he asked the usher's permission to return to the inn, but the officer refused his request and hastily arranged a meal for him instead. "You must have some pity on our lives," he explained, "for if His Lordship should send for you when you are away, that would mean the end of our days."

After dusk the Lord of Liang appeared once more in his reception hall and asked for dice, which he threw again and again on the table, as if he used them to decide some irresolution. Somehow or other he was not satisfied with the results of his throws, for he glared around at his retinue, who trembled with fear.

Finally His Lordship holding the six dice in his palm shouted "Du Xunhe!" and threw them once more on the table. All six ivory cubes turned up with the red four, and the poor scholar-guest was commanded to make his appearance.

The usher led him in, warning him to walk fast, which he did to such good purpose that he involuntarily reached the steps of the dais. His Lordship loudly rebuked him for coming so close to his throne, which made the scholar burst into a cold sweat, mumbling at the same time, "Yes, Sire! Yes, Sire!" After expressing his honour and gratefulness at

拜叙谢讫。命坐，荀鹤惨悴战栗，神不主体。梁祖徐曰："知秀才久矣。"荀鹤欲降阶拜谢。梁祖曰："不可。"于是再拜复座。梁祖顾视陛下，谓左右曰："似有雨点下。"令视之，实雨也，然仰首视之，天无片云。雨点甚大，沾陛檐有声。梁祖自起熟视之，复坐，谓杜曰："秀才会见无云雨否？"荀鹤答曰："未会见。"梁祖笑曰："此所谓无云而雨，谓之天泣。不知是何祥也？"又大笑，命左右将纸笔来，请杜秀才题一篇无云雨诗。杜始对梁祖坐，身如在燃炭之上，忧悸殊甚。复令赋无云雨诗，杜不敢辞，即

being received, he was permitted to take a seat.

Du was still trembling with fright and had almost lost his presence of mind, when His Lordship graciously remarked that he had long heard of the scholar's name, upon which the guest rose from his chair and wanted to fall on his knees to express his appreciation.

"That's unnecessary," roared His Lordship. Du bowed profoundly and resumed his seat.

The Lord of Liang looked beyond to the courtyard, and observed to the attendants that raindrops seemed to be falling. They went obsequiously out of the hall to see and returned confirming the fact, though when they raised their heads they did not notice the presence of a single cloud. The drops were, moreover, heavy ones, and as they struck the eaves, one could hear the sound. His Lordship got down from his dais to have a look himself, returning after a minute or two to his seat.

"Have you, sir, ever seen rain falling without the presence of clouds?" he demanded of Du.

The scholar replied timidly in the negative.

"When there is rain without clouds," His Lordship laughingly commented, "it signifies that Heaven is weeping. I wonder what that augurs."

He commanded that a pen and paper be brought and requested Du to compose a poem on the theme "Rain Without Clouds."

When the scholar first took his seat facing the Lord of Liang, he was embarrassed and felt very uncomfortable, as if he was sitting on burning coals, and now that he was ordered to compose a poem, he dared not refuse. Still keeping his

令坐上赋诗，杜立成一绝，献之。梁祖览之大喜，立召宾席共饮，极欢而散。且曰："来日特为杜秀才开一筵。"复拜谢而退。杜绝句云：同是乾坤事不同，雨丝飞洒日轮中。若教阴朗都相似，争表梁王造化功。由是大获见知。杜既归，惊惧成疾，水泻数十度，气貌羸绝，几不能起。客司守之，供侍汤药，若事慈父母。

明晨，再有主客者督之，且曰："大王欲见秀才，请速上马。"杜不获已，巾帻上马。比至，凡促召者五七辈，杜困顿无力，□趋进迟缓。梁祖自起大声曰："杜秀才争表梁王造化功。"

seat, he managed to finish in the twinkling of an eye a poem of four lines which he presented respectfully to His Lordship, who seemed delighted with the composition, inviting him then and there to dinner.

They parted after spending a pleasant evening together, the royal host announcing that he would later give a formal banquet in honour of the guest, who once more bowed his thanks and retired.

His poem, a specimen of impudent flattery and adulation, said in effect that while the Great Universe remained constant and eternal, an exceptional phenomenon had been noted, namely, raindrops impelling themselves on the glowing solar disc; if in this manner brilliant sunshine and rain-laden clouds lost their distinctiveness, such a miraculous freak of nature could owe its birth only to the infinite creative powers of His Lordship!

From that time on Du became a court favourite.

On his return to the inn he fell ill from fright and nervousness, suffering so severely from diarrhoea that he could hardly rise on his feet. The court usher watched at the bedside and attended to the medical requirements as if he were a loving parent. The next day another official came to announce that the Lord of Liang desired to receive him again, and urged him to proceed quickly on horseback to the palace. Left with no alternative, he made his toilet and mounted his steed with great difficulty, finding on his arrival that some five or six others had also been summoned. As he was very weak from his ailment, he was among the last to enter the audience hall.

"Mr. Du excelled himself in emphasizing in his poem my

杜顿忘其病，趋步如飞，连拜叙谢数四。自是梁祖特帐设宾馆，赐之衣服钱物，待之甚厚。

福建人徐寅，下第。献过梁郊赋，梁祖览而器重之，且曰："古人酬文士，有一字千金之语，军府费用多，且一字奉绢一匹。"徐赋略曰："客有失意还乡，经于大梁，遇郊垌之耆老，问古今之侯王。父老曰，且说当今，休论往昔，昔时之事迹谁见？今日之功名目睹，辞多不载。"遂留于宾馆，厚礼待之。徐病且甚，梁祖使人谓曰："任是秦皇汉武，盖诮徐赋有直论萧史王乔，长生孰见？任是秦皇汉武，不死何归？"憾其有此深切之句尔，梁既有移龟鼎之志，求宾席重言骨鲠之士。

一日，忽出大梁门外数十里，憩于高柳树

creative powers," shouted the lord as soon as he laid eyes on his guest.

This eulogy made Du so proud that he forgot his illness, and almost running towards the dais, and prostrating himself on the floor to thank His Lordship for the compliment.

The lord had a special mansion prepared for Du and bestowed on him clothes, money and many other gifts, treating him with particular generosity.

Another scholar from Fujian, who failed in the government examinations, presented a literary composition to His Lordship on the theme "Passing Through the Suburbs of the Liang Capital," which impressed him deeply with the ability of the author.

"The rulers of old when rewarding scholars," declared His Lordship, "used to say 'each word is worth a thousand taels of silver.' Unfortunately, my military treasury is burdened with innumerable expenditures, so I can compensate the author only at the rate of one roll of silk for each word."

The article in question embodied a conversation between the writer and the country elders, who were made to lavish words of fulsome praise on the lord. He also was invited to reside at the government hostel, besides receiving other courtesies.

Later when the Lord of Liang was burning with ambition to become emperor, he sought for scholars and retainers more honest and truthful than those already in his service. One day he and a number of his retinue went into the country ten miles beyond the city gate, and sat in the shade of a large willow tree, the trunk of which required the outstretched arms of many men to encircle, the branches being

下,树可数围,柯干甚大,可庇五六十人,游客亦与坐。梁祖独语曰:"好大柳树。"徐遍视宾客,注目久之,坐客各各避席,对曰:"好柳树。"梁祖又曰:"此好柳树,好作车头,末坐五六人。"起对:"好作车头。"梁祖顾恭翔等,起对曰:"虽好柳树,作车头,须是夹榆树。"梁祖勃然厉声言曰:"这一队措大,爱顺口弄人。柳树岂可作车头?车头须是夹榆木,便顺我也道柳树好作车头。我见人说秦时指鹿为马,有甚难事?"顾左右曰:"更待甚?"须臾健儿五七十人,悉擒言柳树好作车头者。数以谀佞之罪,当面扑杀之。

梁祖虽起于群盗,安忍雄猜,甚于古昔。

so luxuriant and wide spreading as to give shelter to some three score of men. He and his followers all rested under the same tree.

"What a magnificent willow tree!" he muttered, as if to himself, and looked around at his suite.

"What a magnificent willow tree!" they all repeated, rising from their seats.

"Its timber can well be used to build carts," asserted then the Lord of Liang.

Again, it was echoed by the obsequious followers. Only one person differed:

"Although I admit that the tree is a very fine willow," he said, "for making carts one should really employ the wood of elm."

"What a lot of yes-men have we here," shouted the lord. "You people like to flatter and deceive me by repeating whatever I say. How can the wood of the willow be used for making carts? One must in fact use that of the elm. But you said the other thing simply because I did so. I used to read with some doubt the anecdote of the state minister who pointed to a deer and called it a horse and all his sycophants agreed with him. I can now readily believe the story!"

Calling to his guards he yelled: "What are you waiting for? Off with their despicable heads!" Some half hundred powerful men seized those who had repeated that the willow tree would make carts, charged them with willful and shameless deceit, and slew them.

The founder of the Liang dynasty commenced life as a bandit, and was by nature persistent, ambitious and suspicious, much more so than the other heroes of old. He was,

至于刚猛英断，以权数御物，遂成兴王之业，岂
偶然哉。

moreover, self-willed, audacious and determined in character. It was surely no mere luck or accident that he founded a kingdom and created a dynasty.

三学骂王敬

杨循吉

成化癸卯之岁，太监王敬，以采办药材书籍至江南，所至官司，无不望风迎合，任其意剥取财货，无敢沮者。于是民间凡有衣食之家，悉不自保，惴惴朝夕。又有一种无赖小人，投附其中，悉取富人呈报，或以偿其私怨。敬既恃其权奸，于是大肆厥恶，至及于士类。先在杭州时，使士子录书，或不如意，则出梵经使钞之，得赂而止。

至苏，复以子平遗集，要三学笔录。其多

SCHOLARS VERSUS EUNUCH
Yang Xunji

In the year of Gui Mao of the Cheng Hua period in the Ming dynasty, the eunuch Wang Jing was sent to Jiangnan on an imperial commission to purchase precious drugs and books. Wherever he made his headquarters, the local authorities courted his favour and catered to his wishes, permitting him to extort without protest money and goods from the people. There prevailed, in consequence, no more safety and security for well-off families, who became upset with nervousness and apprehension. Moreover, shameless and unscrupulous minions attached themselves to the eunuch and prepared for him lists of wealthy people to be his potential victims, doing this often out of personal spite.

Relying on his official position and his influence at court, the eunuch committed innumerable acts of blackmail, extending them even to the members of the scholar class. To begin with, as soon as he arrived at Hangzhou he ordered the students to make copies of rare books, and whenever he was dissatisfied with the manuscripts he would hand out as punishment Buddhist sutras in Sanskrit to transcribe. Only when he was heavily bribed did he withdraw such an unreasonable and impossible demand.

At Suzhou he chose the writings of the famous astrologer Ziping, which went to as many as a thousand volumes, for the students of all of the three then existing colleges to copy.

至千余卷,初每生给录一帖,凡录数百帖与之
矣。时方近秋试,复以纸牌呼集诸生,诸生知
其意复欲抄书,不往。敬怒,使人督促三学学
官,学官不得已,率诸生往见于姑苏驿。敬时
坐堂上,其副曰王臣者,立其旁。王臣本杭之
无赖,尝得罪当死。有邪术,能为木人沐浴跳
踉于几上,夤缘进上,遂得宠用,是行实其计。
敬之为恶大抵皆斯人为之,敬特为之尸而已。
时敬见诸生至,责曰:"何不肯写书?"众合辞
对:"向来已写讫。"敬曰:"昨日饭,今尚饱耶?"
遂欲答,学官诸生乃大噪,呼其在门下者皆入,

Each student was ordered to make one copy, and though several hundred copies had been made, Wang Jing was still not satisfied. He summoned once more the young scholars to his presence. As the autumnal examinations were approaching, the students were busily occupied with preparatory studies, and knowing that the summons meant more transcription of books, they refused to appear. The eunuch applied strong pressure on the educational authorities, who, having no choice, led the young scholars, some one hundred in all, to interview the imperial commissioner at the Government Couriers' Station.

Wang Jing sat in the centre of the main hall, assisted by a certain Wang Chen. Now this Wang Chen was a good-for-nothing from Hangzhou. He had committed grave offences deserving of the death penalty, but through bribery and intrigue had become the favourite of the eunuch commissioner. In fact it was his evil suggestions that his patron generally adopted, including the trip to Suzhou. The eunuch was nothing but a willing puppet.

When the scholars, accompanied by the school officials, entered the hall, Wang Jing haughtily demanded to know why they refused to complete the manuscripts.

"We have finished those distributed to us," they replied in a chorus.

"Yes," retorted the eunuch with a sneer. "You had dinner yesterday, but that does not necessarily mean that you are not hungry today."

He then gave orders to cane them. The scholars and school superintendents, highly outraged, commenced an uproar, and called to those waiting outside to join them. In a

指敬面而骂之。敬起而复坐，不能为进退，荒忙失措，仰面偃肩于座上，听其骂。其部下军校，执杖击诸生。走出驿门，遇市薪二束，各执之反击军校。皆散走，王臣知不敌，遁入舟中，众又从而逐之。有却五者，都下恶少，亦王臣党也，被执至城门下，阖门而殴之，几死。时三学生徒，及其家僮仆几百人，既散去。

明日敬召知府刘公瑀，泣而怨之，以为计使诸生骂之。刘公跪拜乞罪，出而访求骂者。自三学乃一时恃其众多，以所访十七人，及诸生皆引见敬。王臣时在侧，乃极口诋诃诸生。不知何人，悉以诸生阴短报王臣，臣悉发之，众

body they shook their fists at the imperial agent and reviled him unrestrainedly. The eunuch repeatedly rose from his seat, not knowing how to handle the angry and screaming crowd. Helpless and panic-stricken in the face of the situation that had developed, he sat staring at the ceiling, resting his head on the back of his chair, while the scholars continued their rioting.

Wang Jing's guards now intervened, beating the students with sticks and driving them out of the building. Outside the students found a man selling firewood. Arming themselves with the same, they commended a counter-attack, scattering the guards. In the fear of his guards being outnumbered, the eunuch sought refuge on his houseboat. The students, in an attempt to track him down, got hold of a certain Quewu, another local good-for-nothing and one of the eunuch's minions, whom they beat almost to death. Finally the students and their pages, several hundred in all, dispersed and went home.

The following day Wang Jing summoned the prefect Liu Gongyu, to whom he made a vigorous complaint, and the latter was obliged to apologize on his knees for the conduct of the students. He went away to make an investigation and succeeded in discovering the identity of seventeen of the young men who took part in reviling the eunuch. These, accompanied by their comrades, were conducted by the prefect before Wang Jing.

Meanwhile some informer had retailed to Wang Chen, the eunuch's evil companion, discreditable stories concerning the private lives of the scholars, and he did not hesitate to make use of the reports in public in his accusations against them,

大惭而出。刘乃引骂者笞于皇华亭下，各二十，具数而已。刘次日召诸生责之曰："王敬家有三条玉带，汝辈小儿，何能与之抗？且说永乐间秀才骂内使，皆发充军，汝谓无红船载汝辈耶？恐械至临清，则俱死尔。"长洲学生戴冠，独抗对曰："死生有命，如何怕得？"遂罢，然诸生又有自书其辈名字，诣敬首告者，益为敬所窥薄焉。方骂时，巡抚都御史王公恕，适至。公严峻刚方，特为天下具瞻，平生恒不喜阉贵。至此诸生惧罪，且诉焉，公曰："既已骂讫，今无

to the great astonishment and indignation of them all. Then the prefect led the guilty rioters away to a pavilion, where each of them was given twenty lashes of the cane — a gesture to appease the eunuch.

Sending for the scholars the day after, the prefect voiced a friendly warning:

"Are you young people not aware that Wang Jing the eunuch possesses in his home three belts ornamented with jade, all bestowed on him by His Majesty? How can you put up a fight against him? In a previous instance in the Yong Le period, a group of scholars once reviled some eunuch to his face and they were consequently exiled to the frontier provinces. Do you imagine that there is not a sufficient number of galleys or carts to convey you men into exile? Know that before you arrive at Linqing Customs Barrier on your way you would all be killed."

Only one of the students, who came from Changzhou, stood his ground. "I am not afraid," he boldly proclaimed. "To me life and death are predestined."

However, the others were intimidated by the grave language of the prefect, and in fact some weaklings turned informers and reported the names of their associates to the eunuch, who despised more than ever the young scholars.

The provincial governor, who held also the rank of president of the metropolitan censorate, happened to be in Suzhou on an official tour of inspection, when the incident took place. He was reputed to be a fearless and an honourable man, who had an instinctive antipathy to eunuchs in high position. To him the scholars appealed, seeking protection from indictment.

如之何？且俟其归，必作奏，亦不过行巡抚巡按处耳，今且勿哗。"诸生大失望，然不知王公密奏已达矣。后敬至阙下，果以诸生事上，至动震怒，果下巡按推治，时敬势方张，未败也。诸生又往告王公，王公曰："此人耳目至多，苏州南北交往之地，兼有二竖在此。（谓织染局有太监二人）既曰推治，安得不答扑？松江僻静，吾已与御史言送彼中狱矣。"巡按时为张公淮亦号有风势，不肯承旨重绳诸生，以是得无苦。然张公亦且未敢决其事，持两可之说以

"Since you have already denounced him to his face," he said, "nothing can help for the moment. When he returns to the capital, he will certainly report the incident to the throne. But the case will after all result in the emperor commanding the provincial officials to handle it in the routine way. So there is no need for panic."

The scholars went away disappointed.

When Wang Jing returned to the capital on the completion of his mission and gave his version of the conduct of the scholars, His Majesty was much angered with them. As anticipated by the governor, the provincial censorate was ordered to bring the rioters to account, However, since the eunuch Wang Jing was very influential at the time, nothing could be done against his wish.

The young men appealed once more to the governor. "This eunuch has long ears and far-seeing eyes," he explained, "and Suzhou is a lively centre of communications, where he has two intimate friends posted in the Imperial Weaving and Dyeing Factory. Since the orders are to bring you people to account, it would be difficult for you to evade arrest and even corporal punishment. Now Songjiang is a quiet and out-of-the-way town; I have arranged with the censor to have you all detained in the prison there."

At the time the provincial censor was Zhuang Huai, well-known for his high moral courage, and he refused to deal vigorously with the accused as the imperial edict commanded. Thus they were spared much suffering. Nevertheless, he abstained from adopting a decisive attitude, one way or the other, but played rather a waiting game. Not long after, the eunuch Wang Jing lost imperial favour and was imprisoned in

待,会王敬等事败下狱,张公力上其事,得皆末
灭焉。

connection with another case. Censor Zhang seized the opportunity to put in a plea for the young men, who were ultimately dismissed with light penalties.

中山狼传

马中锡

赵简子大猎于中山，虞人导前，鹰犬罗后，捷禽鸷兽，应弦而倒者，不可胜数。有狼当道，人立而啼。简子垂手登车，援乌号之弓，挟肃慎之矢，一发饮羽，狼失声而逋。简子怒，驱车逐之，惊尘蔽天，足音鸣雷，十步之外，不辨人马。

时墨者东郭先生将北适中山干仕，策蹇驴，囊图书，夙行失道，望尘惊悸。狼奄至，引首顾曰："先生岂有志于济物哉？昔毛宝放龟而得渡，随侯救蛇而获珠，龟蛇固弗灵于狼也。

AN UNGRATEFUL WOLF
Ma Zhongxi

Zhao Jianzi was hunting in a valley in the state of Zhong-shan. The beaters and guides led the way, while hunting dogs and falcons and their keepers followed in the rear. Numerous birds noted for their flight and beasts for their ferocity fell victim to the mighty hunter's arrows. A wolf, finding itself in the path of the great hunter, stood up on its hind legs like a man and gave a long howl. Zhao, mounting his chariot and picking up his famous long bow, let fly an arrow, which hit the animal in one of its front legs. Giving a yelp it ran for dear life. Infuriated, Zhao gave chase in his chariot, creating a noise like rumbling thunder and raising such a cloud of dust that one could see nothing beyond ten feet.

It happened that Mr. Dongguo, a believer in Mo Zi's philosophy of universal love was stumbling through the valley, accompanied by a lame mule loaded with a bag of books, on his way northward to seek some official preferment. When he saw the cloud of dust in the distance and heard the approaching tumult he was much frightened.

The wolf appeared before him. Leaning its head forward, it asked: "Are you not charitably inclined towards all living creatures?" It continued: "In the olden days, Mao Bao, you will recall, liberated a captured turtle and was ultimately ferried across the water by his grateful debtor, while the Marquis of Sui protected a snake from harm and received as re-

今日之事，何不使我得早处囊中，以苟延残喘乎？异时倘得脱颖而出，先生之恩，生死而肉骨也，敢不努力以效龟蛇之诚。"先生曰："嘻，私汝狼以犯世卿、忤权贵，祸且不测，敢报乎？然墨之道，兼爱为本，吾终当有以活汝。脱有祸，固所不辞也。"乃出图书，空囊橐，徐徐焉实狼其中，前虞跋胡，后恐疐尾，三纳之而未克。徘徊容与，追者益近。狼请曰："事急矣！先生果将揖逊救焚溺而鸣鸾避寇盗耶？惟先生速图！"乃跼蹐四足，引绳而束缚之，下首至尾，曲脊掩胡，猥缩蟆屈，蛇盘龟息，以听命先生。先生如其指，内狼于囊，遂括囊口，肩举驴上，引

ward a wonderful pearl. Neither a turtle nor a snake is as intelligent as a wolf. In my emergency why not conceal me in your bag and save my life? If I should happily escape the present danger I would not fail to follow the example of the turtle and the snake in return for the good turn you do me today in saving my hide."

"Huh," replied the disciple of Mo Zi, "how foolish of you, a common wolf, to get in the way of a noble hunter, and how am I to expect any reward from you when your very life is in the balance? Nevertheless, as a follower of the philosophy of universal love, it is my bounden duty to save you, come what danger may."

He emptied the bag of its contents, and started to replace them with the wolf. He met with much difficulty with the task, what with the dangling legs and the thick bushy tail. Three times he failed, in spite of his conscientious efforts.

The hunters were rapidly approaching and the wolf became highly impatient.

"Sir," he cried, "when one desires to save the drowning from the water or the inmates of a house which has caught fire, one has no time for bowing and scraping, nor does one beat the gong in order to escape from robbers and bandits. Hurry up with your job."

He huddled himself into a heap and assisted as best he could the scholar, who was trying to tie his legs together. He bent his head as far as possible to the tail, which he quickly drooped, adopted the posture of a porcupine, curbed himself like a snail and held his breath like a turtle, so as to facilitate the task. Following the suggestions of the wolf, the scholar finally succeeded in cramming him in the bag, which

避道左，以待赵人之过。

已而简子至，求狼弗得，盛怒，拔剑斩辕端示先生，骂曰："敢讳狼方向者，有如此辕！"先生伏踬就地，匍匐以进，跽而言曰："鄙人不慧，将有志于世，奔走遐方，自迷正途，又安能发狼踪以指示夫子之鹰犬也。然尝闻之：大道以多歧亡羊。夫羊，一童子可制之。如是其驯也，尚以多歧而亡，狼非羊比，而中山之歧，可以亡羊者何限？乃区区循大道以求之，不几于守株缘木乎？况田猎，虞人之所事也，君请问诸皮冠。行道之人何罪哉？且鄙人虽愚，独不知夫狼乎？性贪而狠，党豺为虐。君有除之，固当

after having been tied up, was replaced on the back of the mule. Then he waited on one side of the road for the hunters to pass.

Zhao Jianzi soon arrived in his chariot and not seeing any sign of the wolf, was exceedingly wroth. He struck with his mighty sword the pole of his chariot, cutting off the tip, and swore a terrible oath.

"Let this be a warning to anyone attempting to conceal from me the whereabouts of the wolf," he shouted.

The scholar approached the hunter and fell on his knees: "I am but an ignorant scholar, on my way to a distant place to seek official appointment," he pleaded. "I have myself missed the way, still less am I in a position to show the trail of the wolf to Your Honour's dogs and falcons."

"However," he continued, "your servant has heard it said that it is easy to lose a sheep on the highway because of the many crossroads. A sheep is a gentle animal which even a little boy can manage, yet a strayed one cannot be found on account of the numerous turnings in the highway. A wolf differs entirely from a sheep, and in this valley there are innumerable bypaths for even a sheep to escape. When you seek for the wolf on the main road, may the action not be compared to climbing a tree to capture the eluding fish, or to waiting behind the tree trunk for a hare to break its neck on it? Moreover, the chase is a profession of the huntsmen: would it not be wiser for you to seek their advice than to threaten a chance wayfarer? I confess that I am ignorant, yet I know well the nature of the wolf. It is a cruel and rapacious beast and has for wicked partner the ferocious hyena. If it were within my power I should certainly render you my

跬左足以效微劳，又肯讳之而不言哉？"简子默然，回车就道。先生亦驱驴兼程而进。

良久，羽旄之影渐没，车马之音不闻。狼度简子之去已远，而作声囊中曰："先生可留意矣。出我囊，解我缚，拔矢我臂，我将逝矣。"先生举手出狼。狼咆哮谓先生曰："适为虞人逐，其来甚速，幸先生生我。我馁甚。馁不得食，亦终必亡而已。与其饥死道路，为群兽食，，毋宁毙于虞人，以俎豆于贵家。先生既墨者，摩顶放踵，思一利天下，又何吝一躯啖我，而全微命乎？"遂鼓吻奋爪，以向先生。

先生仓卒以手搏之，且搏且却，引蔽驴后，

feeble assistance, why should I conceal the truth from you?"

Zhao made no response, but turned his chariot and proceeded on his way.

The scholar, touching the mule with his whip, also hurriedly resumed his journey. In a few minutes the hunting party disappeared from view, nor could one hear any sound of it.

The wolf, realizing that there existed no more peril, commenced to stir in the bag. "Sir," he called out, "please note that you must now free me from the bag, untie the rope from my legs and remove the arrow from my foreleg, otherwise I shall soon die."

No sooner had the scholar done what was requested of him than the wolf commenced to show its ugly fangs. "When I was pursued by the hunters," he snarled, "they were hot on my heels and I was grateful to you for delivering me from them. However, I am now terribly hungry, and if my hunger is not satisfied I shall surely die. Now as I look at it, it would be preferable to have been killed by the hunters and made a sacrifice in an aristocratic house, to perishing from hunger at the roadside and being devoured by wild beasts. You, sir, are a faithful follower of Mo Zi, and your guiding principle is to save the world even at the cost of your own life. Such being the case, you surely would not mind sacrificing yourself in order to deliver my poor life."

Thereupon the wretched beast opened wide its mouth, exposing its sharp and powerful teeth, and stretched its claws to attack Mr. Dongguo, who defended himself the best he could with his bare hands, retreating gradually, so as to place the mule between himself and the wolf. Thus the two

便旋而走。狼终不得有加于先生，先生亦极力拒。彼此俱倦，隔驴喘息。先生曰："狼负我，狼负我！"狼曰："吾非固欲负汝。天生汝辈，固需吾辈食也。"

相持既久，日暮渐移。先生窃念："天色向晚，狼复群至，吾死夫！"因绐狼曰："民俗：事疑必询三老。第行矣，求三老而问之。敬谓我可食，即食；不可，即已。"狼大喜，即与偕行。

逾时，道无人行。狼馋甚，望老木僵立路侧，谓先生曰："可问是老。"先生曰："草木无知，叩焉何益？"狼曰："第问之，彼当有言矣。"

先生不得已，揖老木，具述始末，问曰："若然，狼当食我邪？"木中轰轰有声，谓先生曰："我否也。往年老圃种我时，费一核耳。逾年

circled around the mule, the wolf being unable to seize hold of his prey, until both were breathless and exhausted. They faced each other with the mule between them, trying to recover some strength.

"You are an ungrateful beast," complained the man.

"Not at all," retorted the wolf, "it is not that I am ungrateful, but you men were created for us to devour."

The deadlock continued until the sun began to set, and the scholar feared that the fall of night might bring other wolves, making certain his own death.

"According to human custom," he remarked to the wolf, "when two persons argue over a question without result, they decide by asking the opinion of three elderly ones. Let us follow this procedure as we walk along. If all three of them declare that you are justified in devouring me, I am prepared to submit. If not, then you must let me go."

The wolf accepted the proposal, and the two continued on their way. For quite a while they met no one on the road and the wolf was becoming ravenous. Suddenly he saw an old tree by the side of the road, and he proposed to the scholar to put the question to it.

"Plants have no intelligence," objected the man, "what's the use of asking a tree?"

"Just try," insisted the wolf. "Perhaps you'll get a reply."

The follower of Mo Zi bowed to the tree and gave an account of their dispute, ending by demanding to know if the wolf was entitled to devour him. To his amazement a voice issued from inside the trunk.

"I am," it said, "an apricot tree. When the farmer plant-

华,再逾年实,三年拱把,十年合抱,至于今二
十年矣。老圃食我,老圃之妻子食我,外至宾
客,下至奴仆,皆食我;又复鬻实于市,以规利
于我。其有功于老圃甚巨。今老矣,不能敛华
就实,贾老圃怒,伐我条枚,芟我枝叶,且将售
我工师之肆取直焉。噫! 樗朽之材,桑榆之
景,求免于斧钺之诛而不可得。汝何德于狼,
乃觊免乎? 是固当食汝。"

　　言下,狼复鼓吻奋爪,以向先生。先生曰:
"狼爽盟矣! 矢询三老,今值一杏,何遽见迫
邪?"复与偕行。

　　狼愈急,望见老牸曝日败垣中,谓先生曰:
"可问是老。"先生曰:"曩者草木无知,谬言害
事;今牛,禽兽耳,更何问焉?"狼曰:"第问之。
不问,将咥汝!"

ed me it cost him just a small kernel. In a year or so I commenced to put forth buds, after two years to grow small fruit, and at the end of ten years it required the two arms of a man to encircle my trunk. I am now twenty years old. The farmer, his wife and children, as well as friends and servants have eaten greedily the fruit that I produced and sold the kernels for a profit. It is obvious that I have greatly benefited the farmer. After I grew aged, I naturally bloomed and produced less, much to the displeasure of the farmer, who chopped my twigs, sawed off my branches, and is even trying to tear away my trunk as wood for which he will receive from the joiner a handsome price. Old and decrepit as I am, I cannot escape death from the axe and the saw. Compared to my fate, in what way is the wolf so indebted to you as to justify your hope in escaping death from him? It seems to me he has every reason to devour you."

The wolf, delighted with the verdict given by the apricot tree, commenced once more to attack his deliverer.

"Wait a moment," expostulated the scholar. "You are violating our agreement, for so far only the apricot tree has given an opinion and we should have that of three parties."

They again proceeded on their way, the wolf growing more and more irritated, when they caught sight of an old ox sunning itself behind the crumbling wall of a farmyard. The wolf wanted to obtain its opinion on their disagreement.

"No," objected the scholar, "we made a serious mistake in consulting the fool apricot tree, whose ridiculous views nearly ruined my life. An ox is only a stupid animal, what's the sense in demanding its opinion?"

"Do as I say, or you die anyway," was the brutal rejoin-

先生不得已，揖老牸，再述始末以问。牛皱眉瞪目，舐鼻张口，向先生曰："老杏之言不谬矣。老牸茧栗少年时，筋力颇健。老农卖一刀以易我，使我贰群牛，事南亩。既壮，群牛日以老惫，凡事我都任之。彼将驰驱，我伏田车，择便途以急奔趋。彼将躬耕，我脱辐衡，走郊坰以辟榛荆。老农视我犹左右手，衣食仰我而给，婚姻仰我而毕，赋税仰我而输，仓庾仰我而实。我亦自谅，可得帷席之敝，如马狗也。往年家储无担石，今麦秋多十斛矣。往年穷居无顾藉，今掉臂行村社矣。往年尘卮罍，涸唇吻，盛酒瓦盆半生未接，今酝黍稷，据樽罍，骄妻妾

der.

The potential victim could do nothing but salute the stolid ox and repeat his story.

Knitting its brow as if in deep thought, rolling its eyes and licking its nose, the ox slowly opened its mouth.

"The apricot tree was right in its assertions," he declared. "Take my own case: I am now old and shrivelled up and yet I was once young and vigorous. The farmer, my master, sold only a kitchen knife and with the price bought me. When I was young I helped other oxen in ploughing the fields, and when they grew old and feeble and I became stronger, I shouldered all the labour. If my master wanted to go anywhere, it was I that pulled the cart, seeking out the best part of the road so as to travel faster. When he worked alone in the field, and I was released from the yoke, I spent my time in ridding the field of weeds and brambles. I was like the farmer's right hand: he depended on me for his food and clothes. The weddings in the family took place only through my laborious efforts, the taxes were paid with my hard work, and the barn was full due to my contribution. I was easily satisfied — I asked only for a shelter and a place to sleep, like the horse and the dog."

"Formerly," the ox went on, "the farmer had hardly any rice stored up; now there is a large annual yield. He was as poor as a church mouse; now he struts about proudly in the village. In former days the wine jars were empty and covered with dust, my master suffered from thirst, and during half his life he never had a taste of good liquor. Now he makes different brews, drinks freely, and carries himself as the cock of the walk. He wore the short clothes of a day la-

矣。往年衣袒褐，侣木石，手不知揖，心不知
学，今持兔园册，戴笠子，腰韦带，衣宽博矣。
一丝一粟，皆我力也。顾欺我老弱，逐我郊野，
酸风射眸，寒日弔影，瘦骨如山，老泪如雨，涎
垂而不可收，足挛而不可举，皮毛俱亡，疮痍未
瘥。老农之妻妒且悍，朝夕进说曰：'牛之一
身，无废物也。肉可脯，皮可鞟，骨角可切磋为
器。'指大儿曰：'汝受业庖丁之门有年矣，胡不
砺刃于硎以待？'迹是观之，是将不利于我，我
不知死所矣。夫我有功，彼无情乃若是，行将
蒙祸；汝何德于狼，觊幸色乎？"

　　言下，狼又鼓吻奋爪，以向先生。先生曰：

bourer, his friends and companions were only weeds and stones and he did not know how to bow or read like a gentleman. Now he owns a rabbit warren, he wears a broad-brimmed straw hat, he boasts of a broad, handsome belt and appears in an elegant gown: in short, every grain of rice and every fibre of cotton have come from me. But he takes advantage of my age and debility, and drives me out into the open field, where the biting wind hurts my tired eyes and the icy rays of the winter sun almost freeze my shadow. My bony structure looks like a bald and bleak mound, my tears fall like the rain, my saliva drips from my mouth in a steady stream, my legs are cramped and cannot be lifted, while not only the hair but my very skin is falling away — skin which is covered with sores and bruises.

"But worst of all, my master has a jealous and cruel wife. 'Every part of an ox has some value,' she murmurs day and night into the ears of my master. 'The flesh can be eaten as meat, the skin turned into leather, and the bones employed to make various useful articles.' 'You,' she says, pointing to her son, 'you have learned your trade at the shop of the butcher. Why don't you sharpen your knife and get yourself ready for the job?'

"From what I have heard, it is evident that something harmful to me is being plotted and I have no notion as to where and when I shall suddenly be slain. I have rendered invaluable services to the farmer and his family, but they are utterly ungrateful, so before long I shall meet with disaster. Compared to my cruel fate, what claim have you on the wolf to expect leniency from his claws and jaws?"

Just as the wolf made another attempt to seize the scholar,

"毋欲速。"遥望老子杖藜而来,须眉皓然,衣冠闲雅,盖有道者也。先生且喜且愕,舍狼而前,拜跪啼泣,致辞曰:"乞丈人一言而生。"丈人问故。先生曰:"是狼为虞人所窘,求救于我,我实生之,今反欲咥我!力求不免,我又当死之。欲少延于片时,誓定是于三老。初逢老杏,强我问之,草木无知,几杀我。次逢老牸,强我问之,禽兽无知,又几杀我。今逢丈人,岂天之未丧期文也。敢乞一言而生。"因顿首杖下,俯伏听命。

丈人闻之,欷歔再三,以杖叩狼曰:"汝误矣!夫人有恩而背之,不详莫大焉。儒谓:受

the latter perceived an elderly gentleman approaching from a distance, supporting himself with a walking stick. He was neatly dressed, had snow-white hair and eyebrows and was of the philosopher type.

"Please wait a minute," appealed the poor scholar to his aggressor, feeling somewhat relieved at the sight of the new arrival. He turned away from the wolf and advanced towards the old gentleman, falling on his knees and commencing to weep.

"Sir," he begged, "say only a word, and you'll save me from a cruel death."

The newcomer demanded an explanation.

"This wretched wolf," repeated the scholar, "was in danger of being killed by hunters, when he supplicated my help. I succeeded in saving his life at my own peril, yet he insists on devouring me. To prolong my life for even a short while, I made him agree to leave the decision of the dispute to three elders. The first was an apricot tree, which, having little common sense, almost caused my death by his stupid reply. The second arbiter was an ox, which, being only a stolid and unintelligent animal, did no better. I am, indeed, fortunate in meeting you, sir. Perhaps it is the will of Heaven that I, a scholar, should be spared my life. A word of wisdom from you would be sufficient to save the situation."

Prostrating himself on the ground, he awaited the response of the old gentleman.

While listening to the story the white-haired gentleman sighed several times. "You wolf," cried he, as he struck the beast with his stick, "you are in the wrong. When one has received a favour and shows himself ungrateful, such behav-

人恩而不忍背者，其为子必孝。又谓：虎狼知父子。今汝背恩如是，则并父子亦无矣。"乃厉声曰："狼速去！不然，将杖杀汝！"

狼曰："丈人知其一，未知其二。请恝之，愿丈人垂听。初，先生救我时，束缚我足，闭我囊中，压以诗书，我鞠躬不敢息；又蔓辞以说简子，其意盖将死我于囊，而独窃其利也。是安可不咥？"丈人顾先生曰："果如是，是羿亦有罪焉。"先生不平，具状其囊狼怜惜之意。狼亦巧辩不已以求胜。丈人曰："是皆不足以执信也。试再囊之，我观其状果困苦否？"狼欣然从之，

iour would certainly land him in misfortune. Confucius taught to the contrary. If a man does not forget a good turn done to him, he declared, one can be sure that he will become famous as a filial son. This axiom is true even in the case of tigers and wolves, wild beasts though they are. You seem to be an exception to the rule, so with you the happy relation between father and son is obviously something unknown and nonexistent. Away with you, you ungrateful beast, or I'll kill you with my staff."

"Venerable sir," argued the wolf, "you see only one side of the question and not the other. Please listen to me and let me explain. When the scholar tried to save me, he tied my legs and sewed me in his bag. He then thrust his books therein, so that I was terribly cramped and could hardly breathe. Making a long-winded discourse to the hunter, his real intention was to suffocate me in his bag in order to profit himself out of my death. Why should I not kill him?"

The old man glanced at Mr. Dongguo, admitting that if what the wolf complained was true the scholar was perhaps also in the wrong.

The scholar denied the accusation and swore that his entire action was motivated by pity for the wolf. The latter, in its turn, employed much sophistry to establish his case.

"Neither of you," the old gentleman finally asserted, "has convinced me with your biased statements. Only circumstantial evidence will satisfy me." Turning to the wolf, he added, "Let me judge for myself if you were really, as you claim, uncomfortable in the bag, by getting into it once more."

The wolf willingly accepted the proposal and allowed him-

信足先生。先生复缚置囊中，肩举驴上，而狼未之知也。

　　丈人附耳谓先生曰："有匕首否？"先生曰："有。"于是出匕：丈人目先生，使引匕刺狼。先生曰："不害狼乎？"丈人笑曰："禽兽负恩如是，而犹不忍杀，子固仁者，然愚亦甚矣。从井以救人，解衣以活友，于彼计则得，其如就死地何？先生其此类乎？仁陷于愚，固君子之所不与也。"言已，大笑，先生亦笑。遂举手助先生操刃，共殪狼，弃道上而去。

self to be bound a second time and pushed into the bag, which the scholar tied as before and lay onto the back of the mule. As soon as it was done, the old man whispered to the scholar, asking if he had a knife, and if he did, to plunge it into the wolf.

"Would it not hurt the wolf?" demanded the scholar.

"You are a fool to hesitate to kill so ungrateful and dangerous a beast," responded the old gentleman, "though you mean to be kind-hearted. To jump into a well to save a man who has fallen therein, or to divest oneself of clothes to use them to resusciate your freezing neighbour, may be profitable and acceptable to the other, but how about certain death for yourself? You seem to wish to follow such examples. Remember, however, that when charity borders on stupidity, it is no longer a virtue for the wise."

He broke into great laughter, which was joined by the scholar. Then the two of them stuck the knife into the bag and, having killed the wolf and thrown its carcase to the roadside, proceeded each on his way.

再来诗谶记

沙张白

弘治中,闽之候官,有老儒某。博学善文,屡举不第。性迂介,贫困日甚。生一子,不能读书,佣耕自给。年七十,郁郁死。死之夕,取生平著作,题诗其后,嘱其妻善藏之,遂卒。贫无以敛,门人某某四五人,醵金敛之。内某生者,家富,尤笃于谊,偕同学涕泣执丧,瘗之而后去。又时时周恤其孥。

嘉靖改元,江南有某公者,十五发解,十六捷南宫;夙慧神敏,起家庶常;不五年,出典闽

THE OLD SCHOLAR'S REINCARNATION
Sha Zhangbai

There lived in Fuzhou, the capital of Fujian Province, during the reign of Hong Zhi in the Ming Dynasty an old scholar, who was very learned and excellent as an essayist. In spite of frequent attempts, he failed to pass the civil service examinations, and because of his unpractical ways sank deeper and deeper into poverty. He had a son, who was of no account with books and made his living as a farm labourer.

When the scholar reached the age of seventy he died in great unhappiness. On the day of his death he assembled his literary works and wrote a poem as epilogue, instructing his wife to take good care of them. He was so poor when he died that his pupils, five in all, had to make a collection to pay the expenses of his burial. One student in particular, a wealthy man and very sentimental, expressed deep grief, weeping bitterly and following the remains to the grave. From time to time he sent gifts to the widow and the son to relieve them in their distress.

Some fifteen years later a brilliant young scholar coming from an ordinary family made his appearance south of the Yangtse River, passing successfully and rapidly the civil service examinations one after the other and becoming imperial academician within the remarkably short period of five years. He was appointed imperial examiner for the province

试,拔士公明;风檐操笔为程式之文,文不加
点,八闽传通焉。九月之望,值公诞辰,抚按监
司莫不具觞为寿。以翰苑之重,衔命典试,礼
仪宾主,盛绝一时。都人士莫不歆艳,目为神
仙中人,荐绅先达,亦相顾而愧弗如。盖不难
其遇,难其少而遇也。抵暮醉甚,而晋接无间,
避归使舟,闭舱酣寝,戒舟人尽却贺客。

　　比酒醒,已夜半矣。月射纱窗,晶皎如昼;
顾瞻岸崖,清兴忽发。遂潜易衣帻,呼一小竖
自随,乘月信步,不觉数里。所见山川林壑,恍
若旧游,意颇讶之。俄闻哭声甚哀,出自村舍。
公闻之,凄然心动,寻声踪迹之。至一僻小聚

of Fujian, and distinguished himself by his meticulous care and impartiality in selecting the papers of the candidates who attended the examinations, while his own essays, masterpieces of the day, were read avidly throughout the region.

On the fifteenth day of the ninth moon the highest local authorities, including the governor and the chief justice, assembled at a banquet to do him honour, the day being his birthday. The gathering was a distinguished one, as the guest of honour was both an academician and provincial examiner and the other guests the most prominent men of Fuzhou. He was much envied and toasted, being regarded as almost a demigod, not so much because he was the man of the hour, as because he had become one at so young an age.

Tired out by the festivities and somewhat overcome by the innumerable cups of wine which he was obliged to drain, he retired finally to his houseboat, giving orders to permit no visitors to come on board. After some hours of profound slumber, he woke up near midnight feeling much refreshed. The moon was shining brightly through the windows and one could almost believe that it was broad daylight. Gazing at the picturesque bank of the river he conceived the notion to take a stroll on shore. He changed into simple, everyday clothes, and, accompanied by his page, he landed and commenced his walk under the moon, having no particular destination in mind.

For several *li* he wandered along and noted with some new interest the familiar hills, woods, creeks and ravines. Suddenly he heard heart-rending lamentations coming from a nearby hamlet, and much distressed, he followed the sound of weeping till he came to a humble cottage, without even a

落中，一家茅屋数椽，了无篱落。命小竖排闼入视，则有老妪，年且八旬，头髻皓白，燃一纸灯，设野蔬麦粥，祭其亡夫而哭之，词旨悲惋。公揖而问妪："夫人何为者，过哀乃尔？"妪挥涕而谢，掇一破绳床，命公坐。已乃泣告曰："妾拟昼祭亡夫，而儿子远出，迟之至今，度弗返矣。不得已夜祭之。觅杯酒为奠，不可得，用是伤感，顿违夜哭之戒，知不免为君子所讥耳。"公曰："贤夫何人？没来几载？祭既无具，曷不姑俟质明乎？"妪曰："妾夫，候官老儒，才丰命啬，没于弘治某年，今日乃忌辰也，未亡人伉丽情深，虽乏椒浆，不忍不祭，移忌就明，理不敢出。"公闻之愕然。盖其忌辰，即公之生辰，而以岁计之，适二十一。睹妪容貌憔悴，而吐词温雅，有儒家风，且惊且怜之。因问曰：

simple hedge around it. He told his page to knock and open the primitive door. They entered and saw by the light of a lantern a white-haired woman of more than eighty years of age offering sacrifices of wild herbs and porridge to her deceased husband, and weeping as if her heart would break.

The imperial examiner bowed profoundly to the old lady and inquired for the reason of her great sorrow. She thanked him, arranged a seat for him on a broken chair, and related through her tears the cause of her grief.

"It was my intention, sir, to offer sacrifices earlier today to my departed husband, but my son who left for a distant place has delayed his return so I am obliged to make the sacrifice at night. I have failed, however, to find any wine for the ceremony, hence my particular chagrin, although you, sir, must know that it is against the rules and rites to weep at night."

"Who was your husband?" asked the examiner, "how long has he been dead? And if wine is missing for the sacrifice why not postpone the ceremony till tomorrow?"

"My husband was an aged scholar, rich in talent but poor in luck," she replied. "He died twenty years ago, and today is the anniversary of his demise. We were a very happy couple, and although I have little or nothing to offer to his memory, I could not postpone the sacrifice due on this day."

The examiner was struck by the fact that the date of death of the old scholar coincided with that of his birth, exactly twenty years ago. The old lady looked wan and tired, but her language was highly cultured. He felt the greatest pity and sympathy for her.

"贤夫既是硕儒,必富著述,遗编存者,可得见乎?"妪闻而泫然首肯,若有所思。既而告公曰:"妾事先夫五十年,见其精勤嗜学,无间寒暑。瓶无粟,突无烟,淡如也。著述之富,充栋汗牛。制义文字,别为一编。六十以后,每取而读之,未尝不抚几太息,泣下数行。妾恐伤其意,每箧藏之,不使得见。将死前一月,忽燔烈焰,誓将焚之。既而展玩再四,徘徊不忍。嘱妾曰:'一世苦心,难付秦炬,当藏吾棺中,以为殉耳。'言已,欷歔久之。易箦之夕,又向妾索观,题诗其后,而语妾曰:'好藏之,当有识者。'既而笑曰:'文义高深,非吾再来,安识其中神妙乎? 吾生无愧怍,死而食报,易世而后,

"If your lamented husband was a great scholar," he remarked, "he must have left behind him numerous writings and manuscripts; may I be permitted to have a look at them?"

The old lady nodded, mused for a moment and finally confided the following story to the examiner.

"I was his wife for nearly fifty years and can bear witness to his industry and devotion to learning, whether it be in the heat of summer or the cold of winter. If the jar contained no rice or the kitchen chimney produced no smoke, that was of little moment to him. His compositions reached hundreds of volumes, and all his papers written for the civil service examinations were collected into a separate volume. He often took these papers out and read them after he was past sixty. Whenever he did so, he would sigh and tears would roll down his cheeks. Fearing that this sorrow might ruin his health, I hid the book to prevent him from reading it any more. A month before his death, he lit a fire and swore to burn the book, but then he fondled it and hesitated to carry out his resolution. 'The child of my heart's labour during a life-time,' he said to me, 'I cannot bear to destroy by fire. I shall have it buried with me as my companion in death.' Then he would softly sigh to himself repeatedly. On the night of his death, he asked to see the book again, and wrote a poem at the end. 'Put it away carefully: someone will appreciate it.' Then he smiled and continued, 'The contents of my book are too profound for profane eyes. Unless I returned from the other world, who would be able to recognize their excellence? I am ashamed of nothing in my life, and I shall reap my reward after death. In another generation our family will be-

大兴吾宗,令天下寒儒吐气也。'言已,大笑而
绝。迄今二十年,唯门生数辈,抄而读之,他未
有过而问者也。"公闻,急索观之。开卷第一
艺,则发解首墨也。从初迄未,一字不殊,公益
骇然。细加缮阅,则自应试游庠,决科会试,一
发试卷墨裁,论表策判,以至延试策、馆选论,
皆在集中。闽闱五程,亦皆集中语也。最后有
一诗,盖临终绝笔。其诗曰:

> 拙守穷庐七十春,重来不复老儒身;
> 烦君尽展生平志,还向遗编悟夙因。

公读之,恍然大悟,点首浩叹。仰视破屋颓垣,
真同故居。因问姬曰:"向有卧榻,今则安在?"
姬以灯引公入。则朽簀敝衾,尘土坌满,姬拥
破席,卧草荐中。公对之,叹息泣下。姬亦骇
然。问公:"君子,对贫居而饮泣,岂于先夫有

come very illustrious, thus vindicating all poor but worthy scholars.' So saying and with a loud laugh he died. It is now twenty years, but with the exception of a few of his students, who made copies of the book and read it, no one else has ever referred to the work."

After the young academician had heard the remarkable story, he asked to see the book. The very first essay was word for word what he wrote when he took the first examination. Amazed, he ran over the entire contents and found therein every one of the essays which secured for him the higher degrees, his successful palace examination, his admission to the Imperial Academy, and even the subjects he gave to the candidates for their theses at the recent provincial examination. On the last page of the book he found the Farewell Poem:

> *In this poor hut I have spent seventy years*
> *in vain.*
> *When I return, I shall not be the same*
> *frustrated, wretched person.*
> *You will fulfil what I failed to achieve*
> *And find in this book the line of our identity.*

After perusing the poem the academician realized the whole situation. He nodded, sighed deeply, and looking up at the shabby roof and the crumbling walls, felt at home in the surroundings. He demanded where the old bed was. There it stood in the corner with its worn-out mat and old bed-clothes covered with dust, while the old lady's sleeping place was on some straw. He could not restrain from weeping, which astonished her.

"Why do you give way to tears?" she asked. "Is it that

师友渊源之雅乎?"公曰:"非也。贤夫所谓'再来人',即我是也。今日之会,岂繄非天?"妪曰:"先夫之亡,妾柔肠寸断,因闻'再来'之语,私啮尸股,刺指血涂之,以图后验。君子岂有此征乎?"公解靴出股,齿痕宛然,作血殷色。于是,妪大啼泣,公亦悲不自胜。徐慰妪:"夫人无忧,贤夫读书七十年,老不食报,而取偿于吾;吾之逸,贤夫之劳贻之也。苟昧夙因即年少登瀛,皆侥幸耳。吾当大兴前生之门,以酬夙愿,使天下老儒有所感奋,不徒为夫人温饱计也。"妪收泪而谢。公又问:"令子焉往?"妪曰:"先夫没后,妾母子无以自存,幸及门数生,

you are also a student of my late husband and shocked at the misery that meets your eyes?"

"No," he replied, "it is because I am he of whom he speaks as the one who would return. Is it not Fate that has brought me here tonight?"

"When my husband died," she observed softly, "my heart nearly broke. But then he said something about coming back, so I bit him on the leg and stained the spot with blood from my finger as a secret mark. Do you, sir, bear such a clue on your body?"

The academician removed his boot and exposed the leg: the mark left by the teeth was very distinct and red in colour.

The old lady wept copiously, while he, greatly saddened, tried his best to comfort her.

"Madame," he declared, "you need worry no more. Your lamented husband studied diligently during a lifetime and received no recognition in his old age, expecting to receive his reward through me. My success and glory is the fruit of his intellectual labour. If I ignore my efforts, which were really his, then my youthful success would indeed be a strange antic of fortune. No; I shall glorify the house of my previous personality, thus fulfilling his ambitions and giving encouragement to all aged scholars, besides providing for your future comfort."

He asked whither the son had gone.

"Since the death of my husband," confessed the old lady, "my son and I have had difficulty in maintaining ourselves. Fortunately, some former pupils of his come to visit us sometimes, and on the anniversaries offer sacrifices to his

犹敦古处。每当忌日，必遣恤祭。今某生甫登贤书，未暇躬至，故遣儿诣之，不识何以不至？"公问某生姓名，则是科所拔解元某也。余四五人，亦皆新贵。公又慨然久之。

　　既而，东方渐明，姬子已至，后有苍头负酒米钱物，相随而来。其子蓬鬓布衣，一田家庄夫耳。姬命与公相见。询其何以归迟。子言："某解元以座师寿诞，率同年称觞，衙署舟次，两不获见，彼候师，而我候彼，是以归迟。"公顾负米者曰："若某解元仆也？"曰："然。"曰："归语汝主，速来会此。"其仆星驰而去。姬语其子以"再来"故，子欲以父礼事公。公曰："不可，此隔世事耳。"俄而，某解元及同数辈来。闻公

spirit. Today one of them failed to appear because he has just obtained the master's degree, so I sent my son to enquire."

On asking for the student's name, the examiner remembered it as the one he had chosen to head the successful candidates. The other four or five students mentioned by the old lady were also among the examinees who pleased him very much.

Soon it was dawn and the son returned, followed by an old man with rice wine, money and other things. With dishevelled hair and cotton garments the son looked as rustic as any simple peasant. The old lady introduced him to the distinguished guest, who asked why he was late in coming home. He explained that their scholar friend and several of his fellow successful examinees had gone to present their felicitations on the examiner's birthday but failed to find him either in his official residence or on his houseboat.

"Is the old man who came with you the servant of the successful scholar?" asked the examiner.

"Yes, sir," the son replied. "Return to your master and invite him to meet me here," said the guest to the servant. The old man left in a hurry.

In the meantime the old lady explained to the son the significance of the visit of the examiner, and he wanted to greet the latter as his father.

"No," said the guest, "that cannot be, for it has to do with my previous existence."

Not long after the scholar friend in question arrived together with a few other successful candidates, and after hearing the whole story from the mouth of their examiner, all pros-

语,皆顿首曰:"两世师弟,古未闻也!"未几,县令来;又未几,太守室。公对多官,备述所以,无不愕然称奇。公于是首祭老儒之墓,加封树焉。大集烟族,咸有馈赠。其于妪母子有恩者,倍酬之。为妪母子买田宅奴婢,倾赀赈给之。自抚按藩臬,下至公所取士,莫不有赠。妪母子遂为富人,又为其子娶妇。数日间,传遍八闽,自江以南,悉播为美淡。老生宿儒闻之,有泣下者。公以归期急,不及久留,辞妪母子去。终其身往返不绝焉。后其子生子女各五,某解元者与为婚姻。五子读书,三登甲第,最少者,犹以乡贡起家,起至二千石。科名绵绵,为闽中鼎族云。

trated themselves before him.

"Our illustrious teacher and master during two existences!" they exclaimed. "Such a case has never been known in human history."

Later the magistrate came, then the prefect and other high officials made their appearance. They likewise were all amazed at the account related to them.

In the next few days the examiner occupied himself with sacrifices before the tomb of the old scholar, planting a tree in memory of the occasion. Invitations were sent out to friends and relatives of the family to attend a feast, when gifts were distributed to all. Those who had been particularly attentive to the old lady received double portions. For the old widow and her son a comfortable house with adjoining fields and servants was provided, so that they could pass their days in ease, while all the provincial officials from the governor down presented them with suitable gifts. Mother and son were now well off, and the latter took to himself a wife. The news of the strange affair spread like wild fire throughout the province, and many an old and indigent scholar throughout south China felt wonderfully encouraged by it.

The imperial examiner was obliged by official duties to return soon after to Peking, but time and again he revisited the place. The former farm labourer became the father of five sons and five daughters. The boys turned out to be good scholars, three of whom succeeded in passing the metropolitan examinations. Generation after generation distinguished itself, and the family flourished as one of the most celebrated of Fujian Province.

看花述异记

王 晫

湖墅西偏，有沈氏园，茂才衡玉之别业也。茂才性爱花，自号"花遁"。园故多植古桂、老梅、玉兰、海棠、木芙蓉之属，而牡丹尤盛。叠石为山，高下互映，开时荧荧如列星；又如日中张五色锦，光采夺目。远近士女游观者，日以百数。

三月十八日，予亦往观。徘徊其下，日暮不忍归。主人留饮。饮竟，月已上东墙矣。主人别去，予就宿廊侧。静夜独坐，清风徐来，起步阶前，花影零乱，芳香袭人衣裾，几不复知身

FAIRIES OF THE FLORAL KINGDOM
Wang Zhuo

To the west of the Lake Villas was located the Shen Garden, so named because it was the country residence of the scholar Mr. Shen. The owner, a lover of flowers, called himself Flower Hermit. The garden was gorgeous with all kinds of plants, old plum trees, ancient laurel groves, magnolias, crab apple and others, and was especially rich in peonies. Large rocks of grotesque shapes piled one on the other formed a hillock of many terraces, whereon peonies of all varieties and colours appeared like brilliant scintillating stars in the sky on a clear night or like multi-coloured silks and brocades in the sunshine, dazzling the eyes with their lustre and magnificence.

Hundreds of people daily visited the garden. On the eighteenth day of the third moon I also went. I was so entranced with what I saw that I hated to leave when twilight came. The host kindly kept me to dinner, and when the repast was finished, the moon appeared above the east wall. The host retired and I made myself comfortable in the chamber next to the corridor which he had allotted me.

The night was very quiet and I was musing alone, pleasantly fanned by the gentle zephyr. Getting up from my seat I walked down the steps, bewitched by the shadows of the flowers and the soft fragrance that seemed to fill the air. It was difficult to believe that one was on earth.

在人世。俄见女子自石畔出，年可十五六，衣服娟楚。予惊问。女曰："妾乃魏夫人弟子黄令徵，以善种花，谓之花姑。夫人雅重君，特遣相迓。"予随问："夫人隶何事？"曰："隶春工。凡天下草木花片，数之多寡，色之青白红紫，莫不于此赋形焉。""然则何为见重也？"曰："君至，当自知。"因促予行。予不得已，随之去。移步从太湖石后，便非复向路，清溪夹岸，茂林翁郁。沿溪行里许，但觉烟雾溟濛，芳菲满目，人间四季花，同时开放略尽。稍前一树，高丈余，花极烂熳。有三女子，红裳艳丽，偕游树下，见客亦不避。予叹息良久。花姑曰："此鹤林寺杜鹃也。自殷七七催开后，即移植此。"又行数里，一望皆海，红白相间，绿萼倍之。当盛处，有一亭，榜曰"梅亭"。亭内有一美人，淡妆雅度，徙倚花侧。予流盼移时，几不能举步。花

Suddenly a girl of fourteen or fifteen, charmingly dressed, appeared from behind some rocks. I demanded who she was.

"I am Huang Lingzheng, pupil of Madame Wei," she replied, "and because I am clever at cultivating flowers I am called the Flower Maid. Madame has great regard for you and has sent me to fetch you."

"What does Madame do?" I asked her.

"Oh," she explained, "Madame is always busily occupied with tasks connected with flowers, noting their number and varieties, their forms and their colours, whether they be black, white, purple or red."

"Then why should she be interested in me?" I insisted.

"That you will soon know," she smilingly answered.

There was nothing for me to do but follow her, first round the rockeries, then along a limpid creek, bordered by heavily-leafed trees. After a walk of half a mile, the air became somewhat misty, and my eyes met with nothing but flowers, of all kinds and of all seasons, and all in full bloom at the same time! A tree stood in front of us, some ten feet high, laden with flowers, while three maids dressed in red were playing under it. They did not withdraw on my approach.

"That is the famous azalea tree from the Helin Temple," my guide pointed out to me.

After another stretch we faced a sea of plum trees in full blossom, some red, some white. Where the flowers were most luxuriant we came across a kiosk, with a horizontal tablet inscribed "Plum Blossom Arbour," wherein was seated a beautiful girl in elegant but quiet clothes, enjoying herself among her favourite flowers. I was so entranced with the

姑曰："奈何尔？此是梅妃。'梅亭'二字犹是上皇手书。幸妃性柔缓，不尔，恐获罪。"予笑谢乃已。行至一山，岩壑争秀，花卉殆与常异。听技上鸟语，如鼓笙簧。渐见朱甍碧瓦，殿阁参差。两度石桥，乃抵其处。相厥栋宇，侈于王者。傍有二司如官署，右曰"太医院"。予大惊讶，问花姑曰："此处亦须太知耶？"花姑笑曰："乃苏直耳。善治花，瘠者能腴，病者能安，故命为花太医。""其左曰'太师府'何？"曰："此洛人宋仲儒所居也。名单父，善吟诗，亦能种植。艺特丹，术凡变易千种，人不能测。上皇尝召至骊山，植花万本，色样各不同。赐金千

scene that I could hardly continue in my steps.

"That's the Queen of the Plum Blossom," whispered my guide to me. "The writing on the arbour was penned by the emperor himself. It is fortunate that the queen is of an amiable disposition, or she might think you were rude in staring at her."

Walking briskly we reached a spot where the stones and rocks were of bizarre but beautiful shapes and the flowers different from what one daily saw. The birds in the trees sang and twittered merrily, and gradually red walls and green tiles of hall and pavilions made their appearance here and there. Only after crossing two stone bridges did we reach the group of buildings, which rivalled palaces in gorgeousness and dimensions. A little to each side were two edifices looking like offices, on one of which was a signboard: "Hospital." I was greatly astonished.

"Is it necessary to have a hospital here?" I asked Flower Maid.

"Surely!" she replied. "The physician here is Dr. Su Zhi, who is very skilful with the maladies of flowers. He makes sturdy those that are weak, and heals those that are ill: he is known as the Physician of Flowers."

The other building was designated as the House of the Great Master, which was the residence, my guide informed me, of the great scholar Song from Luoyang. A clever poet, he was also a horticulturist and a specialist in peonies, having been able to make a thousand variations — a number of varieties far beyond ordinary imagination. The emperor once sent for him to cultivate ten thousand plants, all different from one another, and awarded him an honorarium of a

两。内人皆呼花师。故至今仍其称。"入门，由西街行百步余，侧有小苑，画槛雕栏，予遽欲进内，花姑虑夫人待久，不令入。予再三强之，方许。及阶，见一花合蒂，浓艳芬馥，染襟袖不散。庭中有美女，时复取嗅之。腰肢纤惰，多憨态，予不敢熟视。花姑曰："君识是花否？"予曰："不识也。"曰："此产嵩同坞中，人不知名，采者异之，以贡炀帝。会车驾适至，爰赐名'迎辇花'。嗅之能令人清酒，兼能忘睡。"予曰："然则所见美女，其司花女袁宝儿耶？"花姑曰："然。"遂出。复由中道过大殿，殿角遇二少妇，皆靓妆，迎且笑曰："来何暮也？"芬姑亟问："夫人何在？"曰："在内殿，观诸美人歌舞、秦乐为

thousand taels of gold, besides conferring on him the title of Master of the Flowers.

On entering the main gate we went along the west passage for about a hundred paces, when we suddenly faced a small garden surrounded by engraved railings and palisades, which I insisted on entering. As my guide was afraid that Madame would become impatient at my tardy arrival she did her best to stop me, but I was not to be obstructed in my wish and we sauntered in.

My attention was immediately attracted to two flowers on a single stem, of magnificent colour and rich fragrance, and to a lovely girl who was enjoying herself from time to time with its rare perfume. She appeared to be indolent and drowsy, at the same time displaying a somewhat voluptuous pose so that I dared not gaze long at her.

On my confessing my ignorance of the flower in question, my guide told me that it came from the Song Mountains and nobody knew its real name. The finder presented the plant to the Emperor of Sui, who happened to arrive at the spot at the time, and the name "Awaiting-the-Imperial-Coach Flower" was given it. When one inhaled its fragrance, I was told, one would be roused from the effects of wine and would forget sleep. The name of the girl who looked after the flower was Yuan Bao'er.

Then we walked slowly along the central passage, passed the main hall, and at the next corner met two young women in lovely dresses coming to meet us with smiles. "Why are you so late in arriving?" they cried.

Flower Maid wanted to know the whereabouts of Madame, and was informed that she was in the inner hall

乐。客既至，当入报夫人。"予遽止之曰："姑少俟，诸美人可得窃窥乎?"二妇笑曰："可。"谓花姑："汝且陪君子，我二人候乐毕相延也。"去后，予乃问花姑："二妇为谁?"曰："二妇本李邺侯公子妾。衣青者，曰绿丝。衣绯者，曰醉桃。花经二人手，无不活。夫人以是录入近侍。"遂引予至殿前帘外。见丝竹杂陈，声容备善。正洋洋盈耳，忽有美人撩鬓举袂，直奏曼声，觉丝竹之音不能遏，既而广场寂寂，若无一人。予闻之，不胜惊叹。花姑曰："此《永新歌》。所谓歌值千金，正斯人也。"

　　语未毕，闻帘内宣王生入，予敛容整衣而

watching the girls dance and listening to their playing of musical instruments. Now that the guest was come, the two young women wanted at once to announce his arrival. I stopped them from so doing and demanded to be permitted to have a peep at the dancers and musicians first.

"All right," was the reply. My guide was told to keep me company for a few minutes, and that as soon as the music ended they would come back to introduce me. I asked my guide who the young women were, and was told that both had been the famous concubines of a young nobleman, the one in green being known as Green Floss, and the one in red, Drunken Peach. Any flower fading or drooping would immediately revive on passing through their dainty hands, and that was why they were employed by Madame in her immediate entourage.

I was then conducted to a split bamboo curtain of the hall, through which I saw fair ladies playing on various instruments, some stringed and others of bamboo reeds, and my ears were immediately filled with soft music. A beautiful girl, pushing bach her hair and arranging the folds of her gown, started singing a song in such a high tone that no instrument seemed to be able to match it. Then suddenly the music stopped and there fell a perfect silence, as if the whole room was empty.

"That's the Song of Eternal Freshness," confided my guide to me. "You know the ancient reference to a singer who won a thousand pieces of gold by singing a song? Well, she is that singer."

A voice called upon me to enter.

I straightened my countenance, arranged my robe and

进。望殿上夫人，丰仪绰约，衣绛绡衣，冠翠翘冠，珠珰玉珮，如后妃状。侍女数十辈，亦皆娇丽绝人。予再拜，命予起。曰："汝见诸美女乎？"予谢不敢。夫人曰："美人是花真身，花是美人小影。以汝惜花，故得见此，缘殊不浅。向汝作《戒折花文》，已命卫夫人楷书一通，置诸座右。"予益逊谢。旋命坐，进百花膏。夫人顾左右曰："王生远至，汝辈何以乐嘉宾之心？"有一女亭亭玉立，抱琴请曰："妾愿抚琴。"一声才动，四座无言，泠泠然，抚遍七弦，直令万木澄幽，江月为白。夫人称善，曰："昔于頔，尝令

stepped into the hall. As I looked up, I saw a beautiful lady dressed like a queen, wearing a pink gown, a tiara of jade, with jade ornaments all over her frock, surrounded by a galaxy of pretty young maidens. I made my obeisance to her; she bade me rise.

"Don't you covet the pretty girls around me?" she jokingly demanded.

I made a gentle denial.

"Female beauty," she expounded, "is only the embodiment of flowers, while flowers are nothing but pictures of beautiful womanhood. Because you are a lover of flowers you have been permitted entry here. You are, indeed, very fortunate. Some time ago you composed an essay urging people not to pluck fresh flowers and I have made a copy of this excellent exhortation, keeping it always on my desk."

I murmured my thanks for her graciousness and modestly took my seat. The Cake of One Hundred Flowers was then served.

Madame looked around at the girls. "Mr. Wang, our guest," she announced, "has come from a long distance; how do you propose to entertain him?"

A girl arose, slim and erect, holding a *ku-chin* (a seven-stringed lute, played horizontally on a table) in her arms. "Permit me to play something," she proposed.

There reigned perfect silence as her fingers ran swiftly up and down the seven strings, and one could imagine, while listening to the soft and placid notes, the whispers of ten thousand trees, with the pale moon glistening over a broad river.

"Once a famous musician played the *ku-chin* by request,"

客弹琴,其嫂审声叹曰:'三分中,一分筝,二分琵琶,绝无琴韵。'今听卢女弹,一弦能清一心,不数秀奴、七七矣。"因呼太真奏琵琶。予闻呼太真,私意:"当日称为'解语花',又曰'海棠睡未醒',不料邂逅于此。"乃见一人,纤腰修眸,衣黄衣,冠玉冠,年三十许,容色绝丽,抱琴琵奏之。音韵凄清,飘出云外。予复请搊筝。夫人笑曰:"近来,惟此乐传得美人情,君独请此,情见乎辞矣。"顾诸女辈曰:"谁擅此技?"皆曰:"第一筝手,无如薛琼琼。"寻有一女,着淡红衫子,系研罗裙,手捧一器:上圆、下平、中空,弦柱十二。予不辨何物。夫人曰:"此即筝也。"

observed Madame after the applause had subsided, "and a
critic declared with a sigh that the music sounded one-third
like that from a *zheng* and two-thirds from a *pipa* (*zheng* —
twelve strings, played horizontally; *pipa* — four strings,
roughly mandolin-shaped) — there could be heard little of
the *ku-chin*. But when I listen to Lulu, every one of the
seven strings reaches one of the seven cubicles of my heart."

Then she called on Lady Tai Zhen to play on the *pipa*.
"Tai Zhen?" I muttered to myself. "Is she not known as the
Flower That Understands Human Speech? I am indeed lucky
to meet her."

She appeared to be a matron of thirty years of age, yet
slim of waist and languid of eyes, wearing a yellow dress
and a jade head ornament. She played a tune on her favourite instrument, and the notes were clear but plaintive,
reaching almost to the clouds.

I requested that some one favour the company with music
from the ancient *zheng*, which I had never seen before.

"That is an instrument that can interpret and transmit the
sentiment of love for a beautiful damsel," Madame laughingly exclaimed. "I can fully appreciate the reason of your
request."

She looked to the right and to the left at the musicians and
demanded who was the most accomplished player. The reply
was unanimous — "Xue Qiongqiong of course!" A girl, in
light red jacket and skirt of silk with open work came forward, holding an instrument round on top and flat beneath,
with nothing in between except twelve columns for the
strings. It was strange to me, but Madame assured me that it

顷,乃调宫商于促柱,转妙音于繁弦,始忆崔怀宝诗,良非虚语。曲才终,又有一女抱一器,似琵琶而圆者,其形象月。弹之,其声合琴,音韵清朗。予又不辨何物。但微顾是女,手纹限处如红线。夫人察余意,指示予曰:"此名阮咸,一名月琴。惟红线雅善此。"予方知是女即红线也。夫人忽指一女曰:"浑忘却汝,汝有绝技,何不令嘉宾得闻?"予起视,见一美人,含情不语,娇倚屏间;闻夫人语,微笑。予遂问夫人:"是女云谁?"夫人曰:"此魏高阳王雍美人徐月华也。能弹卧箜篌,为明妃出塞之歌,哀声入云,闻者莫不动容。"已,持一器,体曲而长,二十三弦,抱于怀中,两齐奏之,果如夫人言。俄有一女,跨丹凤至。诸女辈咸曰:"吹箫女来矣。"女谓夫人曰:"闻夫人延客,弄玉愿献

was a *zheng*. After some minutes spent in tuning the strings, a charming melody was then produced from it.

Soon another girl came and played, this time with an instrument resembling the *pipa*, but with a body round like the full moon. The notes sounded much like those of the *ku-chin* but were clearer and more resonant. I was particularly intrigued by the player's hand, for it was marked by red lines, and Madame noticed my curiosity.

"The instrument is known as the moon-guitar," she explained to me, "and only Red Thread knows how to play it." Thus I discovered that she was named after her remarkable hand.

"My, I have almost forgotten you," Madame, pointing to another beauty, exclaimed. "You are master of a rare art; why not let our guest hear you?"

I rose from my seat to look and caught sight of a girl demure and silent, leaning lightly against a screen, who smiled when she heard what Madame said. I asked who she was.

"Why, she is Xu Yuehua, who can play on the reclining harp *Princess Ming Going to the Wilds*," said Madame. "The tune is a mournful and pathetic one, and anyone who hears it cannot refrain from being deeply moved."

Miss Xu brought a strange looking instrument, with a long and crooked body and mounted with twenty-three strings, and as she played with both of her hands and with much feeling, she produced the effects on the listeners just as Madame described.

Later a young girl arrived riding on a phoenix and was acclaimed as the recorder player. "Having heard, Madame, that you are entertaining a distinguished visitor," she de-

新声。"夫人请使吹之。一声而清风生,再吹而采云起,三吹而凤凰翔,便冉冉乘云而去。耳畔犹闻呜呜声,细察之,已非箫矣。别一女子,短发丽服,貌甚美而媚,横吹玉笛,极要眇可听。夫人曰:"谁人私弄笛?"诸女辈报曰:"石家儿绿珠。"夫人命:"亟出见客。"女伴数促不肯前。中一女亦具国色,乃曰:"儿亦善笛,何必尔也!"绿珠闻之,怒曰:"阿纪敢与我较长短耶?我终身事季伦,不似汝谢仁祖殁,遂嫁郗昙,不以汗颜,翻逞微技!"是女羞愤无一言。夫人不怿,命止乐。忽有嘹喉一歌,声出于朝霞之上,执板当席,顾盼撩人。夫人喜曰:"久

clared, "I've come to offer a popular tune."

As she commenced to play, the room seemed filled with a soft and refreshing zephyr, then banks of multi-coloured clouds rose from the floor and finally the fiery phoenix slowly flew up, carrying the beautiful player away surrounded by clouds, and as she departed, it seemed that one could still hear the diminishing notes of the instrument.

However, on looking more closely I found that the notes came in fact from a flute played by another girl with short hair and wearing a colourful dress. She was not only pretty but glamorous.

"Who is playing clandestinely the flute?" asked Madame.

"It's Green Pearl," was the reply from the other girls.

Invited by Madame to come to the front, she refused in spite of the insistence of her companions.

"I, too, can play the flute," cried one of the girls, also very attractive in appearance. "You need not put on airs."

"How dare you compare yourself with me?" retorted Green Pearl, getting into a rage. "I have all my life remained loyal to Ji Lun, while you married Xi Tan as soon as your first husband died. You ought to be ashamed of yourself to pride yourself on your shallow accomplishment."

Madame was much annoyed by the bickering, and ordered both to be silent.

At that moment a singing voice burst out as if coming from the early morning clouds, and a girl appeared before the gathering accompanying her song with the sharp staccato sound of castanets, her eyes beaming challengingly.

"We have not heard from you for a long while," cried Madame with much delight, "which means that our pleasure

不闻念奴歌，今益足畅人怀。"念奴曰："妾何足
言，使丽娟发声，妾成伧父矣。"夫人指曰："丽
娟，体弱不胜衣，恐不耐歌。"予见其年仅十四
五，玉肤柔软，吹气胜兰，举步珊珊，疑骨节自
鸣，乃曰："对嘉宾，岂能辞丑。"因唱《回风曲》，
庭叶翻落如秋。予但唤"奈何"而已。丽娟曰：
"君尚未见绛树也，绛树一声能歌两曲，二人细
听，各闻一曲，一字不乱。每欲效之，竟不测其
术。"夫人曰："绛树术虽异，恐无能胜子。吾且
欲与王生观绛树舞。"乃见飞舞回旋，有凌云
态，信妙舞莫巧于绛树也。绛树谓丽娟曰："汝
欲效吾歌不得，吾欲学汝舞亦不能。"夫人大悟
曰："有是哉！汉武尝以吸花丝绵，赐丽娟作舞

will be the greater, Nian Nu."

"Oh," she modestly responded, "my voice is nothing; you must get Li Juan to sing for you."

"Li Juan seems too fragile to carry even the weight of her clothes," Madame said, pointing to another girl. "How can she have the strength to sing?"

I looked in the direction she was pointing, and saw a delicate girl of fourteen or so, very gentle in her movements and ethereal of physique.

"I will do my best," she said timidly, and sang the *Song of the Whirling Wind*, and as she proceeded, one could dream of gently falling leaves in the autumn, accompanied by many a sigh of sadness.

When she finished, she proposed that the Tree of Fire make her contribution. This artist could sing two tunes simultaneously, so that listeners would each hear a different song, with the words of each quite distinct. Many had tried to imitate her art but none could learn the secret.

"It may be true that the Tree of Fire possesses a peculiar accomplishment," Madame interposed, "but she cannot be superior to you in singing. Mr. Wang and I should prefer to see her dance." This she did in a marvellous manner, whirling around as if she were on fleecy clouds, so light was she on her feet.

"You are unable to imitate me in singing, but I cannot compete with you in dancing," she remarked to Li Juan when she finished.

"Ah," cried Madame, "now I remember. The Emperor Han Wu had a dancing dress made for Li Juan of soft fluffy silk that would magnetize flowers. One late spring His Maj-

衣,春暮宴于花下,舞时,故以袖拂落花,满身都着,谓之'百花舞'。今日奈何不为王生演之?"丽娟复起舞,舞态愈媚,第恐临风吹去。

忽闻鸡鸣,予起别。夫人曰:"后会尚有期。慎自爱。"仍命花姑送予行。视诸美人皆有恋恋不忍别之色。予亦不知涕之何从也。花姑引予从间道出。路颇崎岖,回首忽失花姑所在。但见晓星欲落,斜月横窗,花影翻阶,翻然若顾予而笑。露坐石上,忆所见闻,恍如隔世。因慨天下事,大率类是,故记之。时,康熙戊申三月。

esty gave a banquet under the blossoming trees and when Li
Juan danced, the flowers attracted by her sleeves fell on her
in showers, so the emperor named the dance the *Dance of a
Hundred Flowers*. Why not let us have the dance repeated
for the benefit of our guest?"

Li Juan commenced her light but complicated steps and the
spectators became apprehensive lest she might be carried
away by the stirring morning breeze.

The cocks commenced to crow and I rose to bid the
charming hostess adieu. "You must pay us another visit
soon," she kindly said, "and in the meantime take good care
of yourself."

She ordered Flower Maid to accompany me home. I took
a last look at the assembled young women and they seemed
saddened at my departure. I also had difficulty in keeping
back my tears.

We returned by a short cut and the path was hilly and un-
even. As I turned to look at my guide, she had already disappeared. The morning star was about to vanish, while the
declining moon was still reflected in the windows. The shadows of the flowers invading the steps of the terraces seemed
to smile at me, and I found myself sitting alone on a flat
stone in the open air.

When I recalled what I saw and heard, I felt as if I had
just come back from another world. That is, however, the
way we feel about most of our happy experiences, which
makes my trip to the Floral Kingdom worth recording.

书周孝子事

钱 泳

周孝子,名芳容,字铁岩,华亭人。其父文荣,弱冠游楚,自楚归娶时,年二十有八。其明年,生芳容。又明年,复往楚。越五载,以省亲旋里,不数月即去。芳容才六岁,稍能记其声音笑貌。后八年,楚中移文至华亭,则客死归州官舍矣,实乾隆五十八年九月十七日也。时芳容已十四岁,祖父母犹在堂,家无毫末之产,赖其母汪,勤事纺织,仰事俯畜,又以门祚衰薄。亲戚皆闻讣而叹,岂能往楚迎柩?乃招魂设奠,丧不成礼。

QUEST OF THE FILIAL SON
Qian Yong

Zhou Fangrong, better known as Zhou the Filial Son, was a native of Huating. His father, Wenrong, went to Hubei as an official when he was a young man, and returned home to get married at the age of twenty-eight. The next year Fangrong was born, and the following year his father again proceeded to Hubei.

It was only after five years that Wenrong came home once more to pay a visit to his parents, leaving after a stay of a few months. Fangrong was then five years old, and afterwards could recall only a little of the voice and looks of his father, for after eight years an official notice received at Huating brought news of Wenrong's death at his post in Guizhou, Hubei. This took place on the seventeenth day of the ninth moon of the fifty-eighth year during the reign of Emperor Qian Long. The boy was then thirteen years old, his grandparents being still alive.

The family was left penniless, and it was through the spinning and weaving of his hard-working mother that the boy and his grandparents were supported. The Zhou family had few male members, and friends and relatives sighed deeply when they received the obituary announcement. It being impossible for any of the Zhous to go to fetch the remains, the funeral ceremony could only be held by invoking the soul of the dead to return to its home, so the obsequies were

既而祖父母相继死,临终,抚芳容叹曰:
"安得汝为寻亲孝子,使我瞑目九泉乎?"芳容
泣而志之。由是始有负骨归葬之念,而连遭丧
病,家亦奇贫,笔耕所出,不能谋半菽之养,欲
行复止者数载。春秋家祭,闻其母哭声甚哀,
而芳容自顾年已及壮,可跋涉险阻,乃自奋曰:
"天下岂有无父之人哉?"遂屏弃荤血,茹斋衣
素,节日用为母氏余粮。焚香告家庙曰:"此去
不得父骨,誓不归矣。"又思途长费重,孤贫下
士,岂能徒手遄征,必至京,随宦者以往。事或

incomplete and very unsatisfactory.

Then the grandparents also died, and on their deathbed appealed to young Fangrong to fulfil his duties as a filial son by bringing home his dead father, so that they could rest in peace in purgatory. The young man wept bitterly and engraved their words on his heart.

The thought of bringing home the remains of his father never left him, but sickness and death caused the family to become poorer than ever. What he made from his pen was hardly sufficient to keep his mother and himself alive, let alone permit of his embarking on a long trip. For several years he made repeated attempts to proceed on the journey but in the end he was compelled to admit defeat.

At one of the seasonal sacrificial ceremonies in memory of the ancestors, he was deeply stirred by the bitter lamentations of his mother, and looking at himself, already a grown man and capable of sustaining hardships on a long journey, he made a resolution then and there. "How can I consider myself a man, when my father's remains are still abroad?" he declared with a deep sense of shame.

He gave up eating meats and wore only coarse clothes, putting aside what was thus saved for the provision of his mother during his planned absence.

"If I do not find the remains of my father, I swear not to return home," he declared as he offered incense before the ancestral shrine. He said to himself that, the trip being long and expensive, it was not possible for a poor man like him to undertake it empty and single-handed. It would be much facilitated by his going to Peking and joining the suite of some official appointed to serve in Hubei Province. There-

稍易，因于嘉庆十七年二月，附漕艘佣书入都。

先是芳容尝为童子师，见人画兰竹，窃效其法，又于书肆中得曹全碑残本，亦时时临仿。既登舟，以其余晷，学书作画，又取官僚中启事尺牍，晨书夕写，以为数者兼习之，庶可藉以游楚也。

六月，抵京师，寓西河沿之泰来店。遍谒同郡官辇下者，泣告之故，皆悯然叹息。许为觅楚馆，初意江汉为天下通途，吴中往仕者，指不胜屈。橐笔幕游，意不计重值，当无所难。乃迟之又久，竟不可得。芳容自思曰，必待游幕往楚，则就道无时。吾为寻亲而出，无论佐人持筹握算，下至佣保兼从，苟可因以到楚者，皆所愿也。又以此意告同郡诸公，亦皆哀怜其志。而楚馆仍不可得，遂拟行乞道路，访求踪迹。

而寓京半年，典衣度日，积逋甚多，寓主人

fore, in the seventeenth year of the reign of Jia Ling, he took passage on a tribute-rice-bearing boat for the capital.

Fangrong had been employed as a tutor and during his spare hours learned to paint orchids and bamboos, and made good progress in the art of calligraphy. He continued his pursuit of the two accomplishments on the boat, besides learning to draft official letters and memoranda, with the belief that these attainments would be helpful to him on his trip to Hubei.

Arriving at Peking he stopped at a small inn, and made calls on metropolitan officials from his home town, to whom he related his ambition. They sympathized deeply with him on his project and promised to secure for him a post as clerk to some official going to Hubei. Wuchang, the provincial capital of Hubei, they assured him, was an important city and a transit centre, hundreds of officials from their native province travelling annually in that direction, and if one did not insist on a large salary, it was a simple matter to secure an appointment. But for some reason or other no such opportunity came to Zhou even after a long wait.

"My purpose," he ruminated, "is to find the remains of my father, and if I wait for a good appointment it may require a long time. If I could reach Hubei, I should be satisfied even if I had to go as a merchant's assistant or as a servant." His fellow townsmen thought compassionately of his ambition, but failed to find for him the humble position he wanted. He decided to proceed on his journey, begging his way.

His stay at Peking had lasted already some six months, and he had to pawn his belongings to pay expenses. The inn-

督促旅费又甚急。时当十二月，同里耿君省修，方以需次在京，甚笃交谊，乃往告其事，求其资，以薄少为出都计。耿以岁将逼除，期于正月初商之。

至时复往，适有朝士在坐，阍者导入傍舍，则故乡数客在焉。坐有戴宝德者，年逾六旬，曾与文荣同客归州，芳容向之号泣叩头，求示以旅瘗处。耿适至，为详述其故，宝德挟芳容起曰："汝即周文荣之子，今已成立，将入楚寻亲耶？孝哉孝哉。虽然，自京师至归州，水陆数千里。观汝形容，傈然一寒士，势不能枵腹往返，其难一也。归州于戊午己未间，遭白莲教之乱，城垣房舍，尽已焚毁。今庐而处此者，皆流移雁户。汝父渴葬乱冢中，兵火之余，安能寻觅？其难二也。孤子当室，家有内顾之

keeper demanded urgently the settlement of the bill: it was in the twelfth moon near the end of the year, when bills must be liquidated.

One Mr. Geng, a neighbour of his in Huating, was then visiting the capital, so Zhou approached him, asking for some financial assistance to make it possible for him to leave Peking. His friend promised to do something after the New Year.

When Fangrong called on him again as instructed, he was shown into an ante-room, where he found some other fellow townsmen, among them an old Mr. Dai, who had been his father's colleague at Guizhou. Falling on his knees Fangrong begged him to tell where the coffin was temporarily deposited, as was customary with people who died far away from home. The host entering the room at the moment repeated the whole story of the young man's case to Mr. Dai.

"So you are the son of Wenrong," observed the old gentleman. "You are a filial child indeed to think of going to Hubei to bring back your father's remains but Peking and Guizhou are separated by several thousand *li* of land and water, and you appear to me to be but a penniless scholar. How are you to undertake the trip on an empty stomach? That is the first difficulty. During two years the city of Guizhou was ravaged by the disorders of the White Lily Secret Society, nearly all the houses were destroyed by fire and the present population consists almost entirely of refugees. Your father's coffin among many other's was buried in the midst of these troubles. How are you to identify the grave after the years of war and conflagration? That is the second difficulty. As an orphan it is your duty to look after the wel-

忧。自宜昌以上，江波绝险，舟行稍一失势，即
下饱鱼鳖。汝纵孝不顾身，其如母夫人倚闾之
望何？其难三也。为今之计，莫如暂且归里，
尽洁白之养。我官江夏日久，宾客多有从归州
来者，当代汝访之。候有影响，即以相告，然后
往寻未晚也。"芳容哭不止。耿复告以将行乞
往寻之事，宝德叹曰："愚哉愚哉。虽然，其愚
不可及也，汝既有此孝思，当为汝图之。今归
州吏目江宁钟君光范，我友也，作书付汝，赍以
往见。钟君乃好义之士，不汝欺也。"是日耿首
倡馈赆，袁方伯秉直，赵侍郎秉冲辈，俱有所
赠，足以稍资屝屦。明日戴持书至，复出路程

fare of your mother, whereas the course of the Yangtse River above Yichang is most dangerous, and the slightest accident would turn you into food for the fishes and turtles. While you may sacrifice your life in favour of filial piety, how about your widow mother, who is watching at the gate for your early return? This is the third difficulty."

"My advice to you, therefore," the old man continued, "is to return to your home and fulfil your other duties of a son. I have been for many years an official in Hubei, and I meet many friends coming from time to time from Guizhou. I will seek for information from them, and if I learn of something definite, I will transmit it to you, and it will not be too late then for you to start on your pilgrimage."

The only response on the part of Zhou was prolonged weeping.

The host then mentioned the young man's intention to beg his way to his destination.

"Folly, oh, what folly!" commented Mr. Dai. "Nevertheless it is a kind of folly difficult to refrain from admiring. Since you are so determined in your filial ambitions, I'll help you as far as I can. The chief constable at Guizhou now is an old friend of mine, and I'll write a letter of introduction to him for you. He is a highly honourable person, and will not take advantage of you in any way."

That day Mr. Geng, the host, proposed to those present to make up a purse for the young man, and all contributed something, which would enable him to but a few necessities for the trip. The next day old Mr. Dai brought his letter of introduction and also an itinerary of the trip.

"From Hankou westward the itinerary goes into detail, so

目一纸,曰自汉口西上,记载极详,不忧迷道。戴因亲老乞改近地,归时当相见里门也,乃敦勉而去。芳容走别耿君,将束装向汉口。

有同寓张某者,金陵人,曾为某郡司阍,熟游齐鲁各官署,适流落在京,乃曰:"子善书画,而无门可投。吾多交游,而无物为赞。盍牵连南行,彼此各有所济? 且南京楚船甚多,屈指可达也。"遂于十八年正月二十四日,相伴出京。一路取笔墨所给,仅足糊口。抵临淮关,张以访友他去。芳容独坐旅舍,愁思凄然,忽念同郡史君本泉,方为颍上教谕,盍往访之,兼问入楚道路? 乃与张分手。

自出都后,芳容日行风霜雨露中,寒燠失度,饥饱无时,精神日靡。由临淮至正阳关,舟

you need have no fear of losing your way," he declared. He himself had asked the government to transfer him to a post nearer home on account of his aged parents, but he expressed the hope of seeing Fangrong later in their native town, together with other words of encouragement.

In the same inn was a man from Nanjing by the name of Zhang, who had been doorkeeper to a county magistrate and was familiar with many government offices on the way between Peking and Nanking. He was at the time also destitute, and he proposed to Zhou to travel together to Nanking first.

"You are good at calligraphy and painting." he explained, "but you have few fiends to approach. I have many friends but no gifts with which to approach them. Why not let us two co-operate? At Nanking you will find many ships bound for Wuchang-Hankou and you can arrive here in a few days."

Thus the two indigent men started on their journey southward, ekeing out expenses from friends and on the scrolls and paintings. When they reached the Linhuai Customs Barrier, Zhang went to look up a friend, leaving Zhou alone in the inn, feeling very depressed. It flashed across his mind that a fellow townsman was teaching in a neighbouring city: why not pay him a visit and obtain some information from him as to the roads leading direct to Hubei?

Ever since the young man left Peking on his arduous overland journey, he suffered much from the hardships of travel, being exposed to the sun, wind, rain and frost, as well as from hunger and changes of climate, so that his health deteriorated seriously. Thus, when he arrived at an inn after

行四日,始投止旅店。头目晕眩,偏身焦灼如火,饮井水数升,神思稍定。次日病不能起。时夏令初届,淮泗间疠疫流行,多朝发夕死者。主人见芳容病状,惧不敢留。欲徙置邻庙,庙故摧颓无主,旅病者移置其中,无不即毙。芳容乃曰:"吾本孤客,主人虑之固当。然吾病虽剧,心实了然,药之可以即愈。且吾有大事未了,为吾招里正,当告以故。"未几里正至,语以将入楚寻亲,迂道往颍上访史君事。又出戴君书及囊中银二铤,曰吾命悬此书,恐病中失去,故以相托。因指银曰:"尽此医病,病如不起,即以具殓,遇松江人过此,以书视之,必有反吾枢者。"里正阅书色动,邀邻医至。医乃寿州诸

spending four days in a small boat and about halfway to the teacher's town, he broke down with high fever. His thirst was unquenchable and he was confined to his bed. It was early summer; the plague was raging in the region and people were dying like flies. The innkeeper was frightened with the sick stranger on hand, and decided to move him to a temple, which was without any priest. Sick travellers were left there simply to die.

Zhou appealed to the innkeeper, saying: "I don't blame you for wishing to get rid of me, a sick and solitary traveller. However, though I am very ill, my mind is quite clear, and I feel sure that, given proper medicaments, I shall recover. I have an important mission which I simply must fulfil, so please call the headman of the street that I may confide my affairs to him."

Upon the headman's arrival, Zhou explained the main purpose of his journey to Hubei and why he was going to visit his teacher friend, showing at the same time the letter of introduction from Mr. Dai, besides two pieces of silver from his bag.

"Please take charge of the letter, as I am afraid of losing it during my illness," he requested of the headman, "my life depends on it. As to the money, please use it for curing my illness, and in case I die, for my burial. If anyone from Huating should pass through here, show him the letter and he will surely take my coffin home."

The headman was very much impressed by the content of the letter, and secured for him the service of a neighbouring physician, who happened to be a student of Zhou's teacher friend.

生,受业于史君者。见书甚骇,叩得其详,曰:
"此吾师之戚,大孝子也。病必无虞,汝辈勿草
草。"时观者甚多,皆怂恿主人相留,不复议徙。
医者以史君故,尽力诊治,日或二三至。七日
热稍退,渐能哺糜,又七日病愈。因急欲登途,
当风薙发,病复大作。自此之后,或因食复病,
或因劳复病,直至六月初旬,始能步履。已留
滞正阳关两月,资斧衣装,又复罄尽。乃步至
颍上,谒史君于学舍,见芳容病容柴瘠,体无完
衣,固止其行。言其次子熙文,将就试江宁,若
同舟以往,则旋松江甚便。以死父而缺生母之
养,孝者不为也。芳容志不可转,史恻然怜之,
乃命作书画数十幅,以己名刺,遣斋夫遍投门
下诸生。诸生有答者,馈银或三四钱,或五六
钱,聚之得二十余两。因具衣履,别史君而行。

　　自颍上至汉口,道经商雒黄麻间。一路人
烟稀少,崇岩巨岭,绵亘千余里,为车马所不通

"Why, my patient is a noted filial son and related to my teacher," he exclaimed. "I'll do my best to cure him, and you people must not neglect him."

A crowd had gathered together by that time, and the innkeeper was persuaded not to expel his guest. Meanwhile, the doctor took very good care of Zhou, coming to see him two or three times a day. After a week his temperature became normal and in a fortnight he was fully recovered. Unfortunately, in his haste to resume his journey, he shaved his head in a draught, and got a relapse. His ailment continued off and on for some weeks, and it was already the beginning of the sixth moon when, moneyless and almost clothesless, he walked the rest of the way to see Mr. Shi, his teacher friend.

Mr. Shi seeing the ravages of his visitor's illness and the desperation of his conditions advised the latter strongly to abandon his quest. His own second son was proceeding to Nanking for the examinations, and the two, he urged, could go in the same boat; from Nanking he could easily return to his home. Moreover, he tried to dissuade Zhou on the ground that filial piety obligated no one to seek his dead father at the cost of leaving his mother to starve.

However, the young man refused to deviate from his set purpose, so Mr. Shi told him to make a few scrolls and paintings and had them sent to his well-off students, together with his own letters appealing for their patronage. In this way some twenty taels of silver was raised, with which Zhou bought some clothes and started for Hubei again.

The country he had to traverse before reaching Hankou, his next stop, was mountainous, wild and uninhabited. The

行者,惟乘竹轿。轿日费千钱,非有力者不能也。加以秋暑未退,草木正盛,瘴烟毒雾,终日不一开霁。又滑县邪教将乱,奸人乘间伏莽,道多梗塞。芳容则麻鞋短服,日行三四十里。遇无旅舍处,辄据石倚树,露宿草间。或风雨骤至,往往淋漓达旦。尝宿山家檐下,梦中为物所惊觉,则有长蛇一条,黑质白章,从领穿袖而出,芳容悸不敢动。又夜行青石岭下,山半双灯炯然,以为人也,呼之灯忽不见。听猛虎一声,遮道而立,因窜身荒堑间以免。又山蹊遇雨,水势汹汹,赤脚行石齿中,忽踬决肤裂,流血不已。时有卖草帽者数人同行,有地名往流集者,芳容至此,不能复前。数人先去,未几有两人仓皇而反曰:"过此八九里,峰回路转处,突出十余人,梃刃交下,劫所有以去。已毙一人,余各他窜。吾所以逃归者,欲愬之官也。"芳容骇甚,明日俟多人为伴,始敢前行。

only means of conveyance was by bamboo sedan-chairs, but the cost was prohibitive to our lone traveller. Due to the luxuriant vegetation and summer heat, the area was covered with a pall of unhealthful miasma, hiding even the sun. the roads, if they could be called such, were infested with robbers, while inns were few and far between.

In short clothes and hemp sandals, Zhou would cover some ten miles or so daily, and where he found no inn or shelter, would sleep on the ground or under trees; in rainy weather he would be soaked to the skin. Once sleeping under the eaves of a mountain cabin, he was awakened by something in his dreams: a black and white snake went down the nape of his neck and crawled out of his sleeve! On another occasion, walking at night he perceived what he believed was a pair of lanterns. He called out. No human voice answered, but a tiger jumped on to the road in front of him. Only by throwing himself into a ditch did he escape the king of beasts.

Owing to the heavy rains the mountain paths were flooded, so his bare feet were often cut by the sharp stones, leading to much bleeding. At this time he was travelling in the company of some pedlars who sold straw helmets. A few of them stopped to rest, while others pressed forward to the next village. It was not long before two of them rushed back in sorry shape, because the party had encountered a dozen bandits who had robbed them of the little they had. One of their comrades was killed and the others scattered, they having fled back to warn those who were resting. Under the circumstances Zhou and the others remained where they were till some more travellers came along, before they ventured to

山中所经危险之地,不可胜数。及抵汉口,则已清风戒寒矣。

前在京时,戴君以路程目相赠,凡江途夷险,城市疏密,及停帆、易艇、旅行,水宿之事,无不详备。遂依目中所载,附估客船以行。

适公安水发,不能前进,枉道由洞庭湖,折而西上。舟中侧席而坐,临食而叹,时时以泪洗面,或竟夜不眠,咄咄自语。同舟者怪而问之,不以实告也。

至宜昌,空囊如洗,饮食俱缺,检随身物凡值一钱半锱者,悉付质库,得钱一千余文。易舟就道,是夕芳容梦其父形貌如昔,诫曰:"明日上滩,汝宜留意。"明日过青滩,水势狂悍,石角参错,波涛间,触舟舟漏,几沉没江中。既出险,各贺重生。乃于九月初一日,抵归州城。下自宜昌浮江,上溯滩。滩梯接,势若建瓴。归州城濒江设险,鸡鸣犬吠,恍在霄汉。明初

continue on their journey. Such painful and dangerous experiences were many and frequent, and by the time he reached Hankou the cold weather had already commenced.

Mr. Dai's itinerary was, indeed, very conscientiously compiled and gave full particulars as to the best routes to be followed from Hankou westward, the distances between cities, places where the traveller must tranship, and hotels and inns to spend the nights on the way. Zhou booked a seat on a passenger boat, but on account of the floods the boat had to follow a roundabout route, by the Dongting Lake. He felt miserable on the boat, not being able to eat or sleep. But, when questioned by his fellow passengers he did not reveal his objective.

By the time he arrived at Yichang he was once more penniless. Selling all available personal articles of any value, he raked together a thousand small cash and resumed his ascent of the Yangtse River. That night he dreamed that his father spoke to him in a warning way: "Tomorrow the gorges begin; be careful."

Sure enough, the rapids were unusually perilous, and late in the next day the boat ran into a rock in midstream and all on board were only short of being drowned. Ultimately, the boat arrived at Guizhou, on the first day of the ninth moon.

From Yichang upwards the rapids succeeded one another like the rungs of a ladder and the town of Guizhou, located near the upper end of the Yangtse Gorges, occupied a point of high vantage. When one listened to the crowing of cocks and barking of dogs in the town from a distance down the river, one would believe it to be up in the clouds. The city walls and their battlements were built in the early years of the

崇墉屹立，后为张献忠所夷，乃栅要害守之。近复毁于寇乱，重事版筑，官府方招集流亡，疏节阔目，与民生聚。由是闾阎阛阓，较旧制更严且整。

　　芳容就寓州署之侧，乃持戴君书，谒吏目钟君。钟见书骇然，一再阅之，蹙然曰：“此乡自被寇后，城郭人民，皆非畴昔。即十年前事，知者甚鲜，况二十年耶？土著之民，墓田丙舍，皆已为谷为陵，矧旅槥耶？汝既来此，且少弛担簦，当行寻郊外，裹草根片土，招魂归葬。于孝子之心，亦可无憾。如欲求真骨以归，正恐徒劳无益耳。”芳容固求公访之，因遍询州役，及城内外琳宫佛宇，讫无知者。

Ming dynasty, but were razed to the ground during the years of rebellion led by Zhang Xianzhong. The wooden barriers set up later around the key points of the city were again burned down in recent riots. Reconstruction of the town had just been commenced, some headway had been made in the rehabilitation of the refuges, and gradually the town was picking up prosperity.

No sooner had Zhou lodged himself in an inn near the magistracy than he went and called on the chief constable with the letter of introduction from Mr. Dai. The officer read the letter over and over again, and was astounded at the contents.

"Ever since the war with the rebels, the lay-out of the town and its population have entirely changed," he said mournfully. "Few people know anything about events which occurred here ten years, still less of twenty years, ago. Even the cemeteries and family graveyards of the local people have been turned into fields and ponds; how is one to trace the coffin of a stranger? However, young man, since you are already here, rest up a little while and then we may go together to outside the city limits, where you can wrap up a piece of sod, invoke the spirit of your lamented father and return to your home. In this way you will have fulfilled more than the usual obligations of a filial son. It would be an utterly vain attempt, I am afraid, to find the actual remains of your beloved father."

Absolutely undaunted, Zhou insisted upon making thorough enquiries. The chief constable had to accede to his request, and every policeman, every temple and other depositaries of coffins were questioned about the matter, but noth-

州有老役徐某,避乱居巴巫间,常回州应役。一日至署,芳容适在座。钟问曰:"前二十年浙有黄公钟岱官此,汝知之乎?"曰:"知之"。曰:"黄有幕客周,病殁于署,汝知之乎?"曰:"知之。某年某为役总,董率各役。黄本官系六月到任,携幕客三人,一戴,一许,一周。周到署已病,一童子侍汤药。一日童子唤某入,则已气绝床上,药瓯犹在手也。时黄本官,与戴姓者,在省未归,惟许姓为具棺殓。虽事越二十余年,犹能记其髣髴。"芳容闻之,感泣不能止。急询瘗埋之所,曰似在东关外骨坟塘侬稀偏左,自遭教匪蹂躏,恐迷其处矣。钟谓芳容曰:"今略得影响,子宜移寓就近。东关外有太平庵者,可往居之。明当遣徐某为导,求其

ing materialized.

One day an aged constable from the country who used to come to the town to serve for a certain period turned up at the magistracy. He was asked if he remembered the Magistrate Huang from Zhejiang Province and one of his secretaries who died in office and the replies to both questions were in the affirmative.

"Of course I know," replied the veteran constable. "I was captain of the county police that year when Magistrate Huang arrived with three secretaries, one of whom was Mr. Zhou. The latter was already ill on reaching Guizhou and a boy-servant looked after him. One day the boy sent for me, and when I went to the house I found Mr. Zhou already dead, the medicine cup still in the boy's hand. One of his colleagues attended to the funeral and burial, as the magistrate and the third secretary had gone on a visit to the provincial capital. Although twenty years have elapsed, I can still remember a little the looks of this Mr. Zhou."

Young Zhou who was there listening to the details of his father's death was overwhelmed with sorrow and at the same time with contentment. He eagerly asked if the old man recalled the place of burial. The latter believed that it was in a cemetery outside the East Gate, a little to the left, but after all those years of devastation, he seriously doubted if the tomb could be located.

"Now that we possess some inkling of the tomb," observed the chief constable, "you might as well move your lodging as near to it as possible. There is the Taiping Temple outside the East Gate, where you can stay. Tomorrow I'll send Captain Xu to guide you in finding the grave."

殡所。"芳容乃移寓庵中。

次日乞徐为导,至骨坟塘,塘去城一二里,荒山乱草,四周立石为界,为商旅丛葬之所。芳容伛偻草际,求之不可得。次日复往寻觅,日将趺,仍不可得。芳容自念曰:"此间四五里,白骨如莽,陈陈相因。拟尽半月之功,穷索瘗所。吾万里远来,不得父骨,当投江而死耳。"正然疑间,忽见十余步外,片石半没土中。亟掊土视之,石上字凡三行,中一行云,清故周文荣,系江苏松江府华亭县人;左行云,殁于癸丑年九月十七日卯时;右行云,某年月日同人公立。芳容心喜极而悲,号恸不能起,欲露宿冢上。徐某谓地多豺虎,常白昼啮人,因挟芳容归寓。

明日趋告钟,钟欣然曰:"亲骸既获,大志已慰。若迎归故里,则江路辽远,约略计之,非

The following day Zhou, accompanied by the guide, went to a rising ground overgrown with weeds half a mile outside the East Gate, where travelling merchants and strangers in the old days used to be buried. In spite of assiduous search and reading of all the tombstones meeting his eyes, he failed to identify his object. At twilight of the third day he was still engaged in his search.

Here in an area of a square mile human bones were as plentiful as weeds. "If necessary, I'll devote half a month's time to locate the tomb," he thought to himself. "If I should fail, after having travelled so many thousand miles, there can be but one ending — I shall jump into the river."

At that very moment he saw a stone tablet some ten yards away, jutting out of the ground to about half its height. Hurrying over and pulling it out of the earth, he discovered three vertical lines of characters engraved on the stone, the middle one stating unmistakably that the departed was Zhou Wenrong of Huating County, Songjiang Prefecture, the line on the right the date of his death, and the one on the left that the stone was erected by his friends and colleagues. Zhou was both overjoyed and heart-broken at the discovery and could hardly raise himself from the ground. He wanted to spend the night on the grave, but the old guide dragged him away, saying that the place was infested with wild beasts that attacked people often in broad daylight.

The chief constable felt very happy when informed of the turn of events. "Now that you have found the remains," he advised the young man, "you should be completely satisfied. I don't think it's practical to convey them back home, for the voyage is long and costly, requiring at least two hun-

二百金不可。且掩土已久，不如无动。南宋大儒，多有父母异葬者，可法也。"芳容决意负骨归终，钟不能止，曰此事宜告本州。次日乃告州牧刘公清祥。刘悯芳容志，命里正与伍伯为助。钟亦遣人来，预具水瓮二，黄布囊一，油纸数幅，绵纸八番，蚕绵一束，线一绚，及笔墨疏布小刀之属，择于重九日登山收骨。

　　是日天良气清，雇土工二人，持祭物偕往。至则里正州役咸在，乃陈祭冢下，启土见棺，则前和已朽，触处糜滥，棺破而骸见。芳容擗踊哀号，以口衔左臂肉，右手持刀割之，用力过猛，皮裂及肘。又割之，以肉抵父颔龋间，辄胶合如漆。左臂血沾渍骨上，亦深入不流。乃掬泥掩创，裹以疏布，匍匐拾骨。伍伯展油纸陈之，土工次第加纩，裹以绵纸。芳容乃以血和墨，寸别件记，凡若干股，装为一囊，护以绵被。又以余墨拓石上字数纸，为归日征信。然后掩石入土。归州江山雄奇，东郭尤胜。时登高者

dred taels. Besides, why disturb them, after they have been interred so long? You can well follow the example of the noted scholars of the Song Dynasty, who frequently had their parents buried in separate localities."

But the young man was obdurate, and there was no way of diverting him from his purpose.

The matter was reported to the magistrate, who sympathized with the young man's aspiration, sent the local headman to assist him in unearthing and gathering the bones.

Equipped with two jars, one yellow bag, oil and ordinary wrapping paper, pieces of silk, string, writing implements and so on, the party went to the grave on the ninth day of the ninth moon to carry out their pious task. After appropriate sacrifices the coffin, half decomposed, was opened, and the skeleton appeared. Zhou was so moved by the sight that he took out a knife and removed a piece of flesh from his arm to seal up the jaw of his dead father. After dressing the wound with some earth and cloth, he fell down on his knees, picked up the bones one after the other, wrapped them separately and noted down their particulars on the wrapping paper. The packages were then solemnly and respectfully placed in the yellow bag, which was further protected with heavy cloth. Then he took rubbings of the engraved characters on the tombstone, to be taken home as evidence of his find. As a final act, the tombstone was carefully buried in its original spot.

Now Guizhou was noted for its landscape, with its lovely hills rising from the river bank, and outside the East Gate the scenery was specially pretty. It being the tradition for the people to visit the elevated spots on the "Double Ninths,"

数十百人，闻有此事，至骨坟塘，环而视之，无
不泪下称叹。

　　乃负骨至太平庵，冀卖书画作归计。而穷
途踯躅，费无所出。有湖州商人某亦来游，叩
及里居，因曰："今游击张将军廷国，亦松江人
也。子如未相识，当为之介绍。"乃谒将军于江
上，各叙故旧，并告以不能归骨之故。将军恻
然，许为谋之。次日钟欢笑而至曰："大好遭
际，昨有宴会，文武官皆集。张将军以汝事告
刘公，公谓孝行如某，而困不能归，官斯土者之
咎也。首赙白银五两，余官皆三两，幕客三人
各二两，已二十余两矣。张将军赙钱十缗，遣
旗牌檥江船送至汉口，刻期于三日后起程。岂
非大好遭际哉？"芳容惘然不知所对。因遣仆
导芳容谢刘公，刘延至书室，命以隶写孝经数
幅，曰："藏此孝子手迹，可为吾子孙劝也。"又
遍谢文武诸官。芳容临行，钟君持刘公官封

many townspeople were enjoying themselves in the vicinity of the cemetery, and when they heard of what was happening, they came in crowds to watch the ceremony, expressing their admiration and amazement.

Zhou returned to his temple lodging with his precious packages and commenced to plan his return trip, hoping to cover expenses by selling specimens of his calligraphy and painting. But it was difficult to raise sufficient funds in this way for the purpose. Fortunately through a chance acquaintance he was introduced to a General Zhang, also from Songjiang, who promised his help.

The following day the chief constable called and congratulated his young friend, reporting that at a dinner the previous night, where were gathered all the local officials, General Zhang mentioned Zhou's financial difficulty to the magistrate, who declared at once that if such a filial son failed in his mission due to shortage of funds, he as magistrate would be the first one to be thoroughly ashamed. Thereupon he contributed five taels of silver to a fund to assist Zhou. Others followed suit, and in a few minutes more than twenty taels was raised, besides a gift of ten strings of cash from the general. The latter would also commandeer a boat to convey the young man and his belongings to Hankou, starting within three days.

Calling on the magistrate to present his heartfelt thanks, Zhou was requested to copy for him in ancient script several pages of the *Classic on Filial Piety*, so that he would always treasure the handwriting as coming from a remarkable young man and pass it on to his children for their edification. The magistrate gave him an official communication addressed to

书一通，俾归投华亭县，互相咨照。

遂白衣冠，负骨登舟，居人出郭争视，途为之塞。时嘉庆十八年九月二十日事也。

及解缆，风顺水急，不数日即达汉口。作书托旗牌谢张将军。乃由汉口易舟而东，舟人于柁楼祀金龙神甚虔，芳容亦早晚焚香稽首，祷求默助。半月余，竟达里门，急省其母。虽望眼将穿，犹幸康健如昔。

因寄骨城东佛舍，悬所拓石刻字于前，扶老母哭而祭之。闻者皆为酸鼻。既而卜兆于祖墓之旁营治井椁，即于十一月初九日安葬。时戴君宝德，改官金华尉，乞假，省亲。适芳容负骸骨归，亦来送葬，则又相顾诧为奇绝也。

the Magistrate of Huating, containing a full account of Zhou's visit to Guizhou and its successful termination.

Wearing the white hat and white clothes of mourning, Zhou embarked in triumph for his trip down the river, his departure being witnessed by hundreds of the residents who crowded the streets and the river bank. This happened on the twenty-sixth day of the ninth moon in the eighteenth year of the Jia Qing period. The boat arrived in a few days at Hankou, the wind being favourable and the current very swift.

At Hankou Zhou transhipped, joining the boatmen in their daily offer of incense to the Deity of the Golden Dragon, and in a fortnight reached his home. His mother, though impatient and worried at his lengthy absence, was as healthy as ever.

The bones were first deposited in a temple together with the paper rubbings from the tombstone, and then buried properly in their ancestral graveyard.

Having delivered the official communication from Guizhou to the local magistrate, Zhou was invited to the latter's office, where he was highly commended for his virtues. Later the affair was reported even to the throne, and the Zhou family was duly honoured.